Praise for the first edition of the Homeschool Math Manuals:

"Each book is like a visit from a veteran homeschooling mom. Informal and easy to read, these small volumes are packed with helpful tips and ideas for new and experienced homeschoolers."

—*Home Education Magazine*

"Denise Gaskins gives you scores of simple ideas that make math relevant, understandable, and fun...ever-so-practical..."

—*Homeschooling Today*

"I really like your products. You have kept them simple, easy to understand, and very helpful."

—*Llewellyn B. Davis, The Elijah Company*

"Here's how to break out of the textbook mold and keep your kids enthused about mathematics."

—*Debra Bell, Home School Resource Center*

"These are great ideas to encourage math in our kids' lives. What fun!"

—*Rebecca Ellis, homeschooling mom*

"Thank you for the assistance these books have been to me—a first year, novice homeschooler. I hope new books will be forthcoming!"

—*Maureen O'Brien, homeschooling mom*

"I was an honor student in education at the University of Illinois, but I never learned how to teach math. Thank you for your clear and motivating guides."

—*Jena Borah, homeschooling mom*

"I *like* math!"

—*10-year-old homeschooler*

Homeschool Math Manual 2

Master the Math Monsters

Factors, Fractions, and Long Division

Second Edition

Denise Gaskins

Tabletop Academy Press

For Marilyn,
who kept asking questions,
and for Jonathan,
who figured out how to divide with fractions.

Master the Math Monsters: Factors, Fractions, and Long Division

Library of Congress Catalog Card Number: 00-190130

ISBN 1-892083-12-4

Tabletop Academy Press
8487 Rosedale Road, Blue Mound, IL 62513-8135
tabletop@fgi.net

Beware—Math Monsters Ahead!

- **They crash into the mind like a truck against a brick wall.**
- **They trample self-confidence into the mud.**
- **They cause headaches and stomach cramps in otherwise healthy individuals.**
- **They brainwash children with the "I can't do it" mantra.**
- **Who are they? The math monsters!**

Math monsters are those scary topics of textbook arithmetic, things like borrowing, factors, and long division. Common denominators give children nightmares. And who wants to think about decimals or percents or ratios? *Aaargh!*

But math monsters need not frighten your children. The secret to handling the math monsters is to take them on a little at a time and to introduce the topics with hands-on games and manipulatives.

After all, most children enter school with a natural feel for mathematical ideas like counting, adding, or sharing out a plate of cookies between friends. The most effective homeschool math teacher builds on her children's innate understanding of math.

But even the best teacher occasionally finds herself trying to clarify an arithmetical procedure to a confused student. And sometimes the more she tries to make it clear, the more tangled her own mind becomes. How can she explain principles she never fully understood herself?

If teaching fractions makes you frantic and you are paranoid about percents, you are not alone.

This book will help you master the real killers of elementary and junior high school textbook arithmetic, those monster topics that go *thump!* in the mind. You will learn how to teach place value through hands-on play, and subtraction without borrowing. You will meet the teacher's best friend, base ten blocks. And you will learn to deal with those dastardly fractions—even when they are in disguise as decimals or percents or ratios.

Homeschool Math Manuals

This is the second of five Math Manuals that will be available from Tabletop Academy Press. Others in the series are:

1—Aha! How to Teach Math So Kids Get It

You can lay a foundation for success in math by building your students' problem-solving skills. Discover how toys, games, and library books can help children of all ages enjoy the challenge of creative mathematical thinking—and when to make the transition to textbook math.

3—Algebra for Anyone: Getting a Handle on Abstract Math

Children can begin to learn algebra as early as third grade using manipulatives, but without them even high school students may struggle. Step-by-step instructions and examples take you from solving simple equations to factoring quadratic polynomials.

4—Gotcha! Strategy Games for Math and Logic

When children play strategy games, they learn to enjoy the challenge of thinking hard. Introduce your family to more than 20 games you can enjoy at home or in the car.

5—Let's Play Math: Number Games with a Deck of Cards

Forget flashcards and worksheets. Your children can practice their math facts by playing cards. Beginners will enjoy simple addition and place value games, while more advanced students will be challenged to master fractions and negative numbers. [Let's Play Math is still in the works—publication date not set. Please write if you would like your name on the waiting list. I will let you know as soon as it goes to press.]

I hope these books help to make math your children's favorite subject. If you have more questions about mathematics or about my books, I would love to hear from you.

—Denise Gaskins

Table of Contents

If you could lead through testing,
the U.S. would lead the world
in all education categories.
When are people going to understand
you don't fatten your lambs
by weighing them?

—Jonathan Kozol[1]

***

I don't like that sort of school...
where the bright, childish imagination
is utterly discouraged...
where I have never seen among the pupils,
whether boys or girls,
anything but little parrots
and small calculating machines.

—Charles Dickens[2]

***

We cannot hope
that many children will learn mathematics
unless we find a way
to share our enjoyment
and show them its beauty as well as its utility.

—Mary Beth Ruskai[3]

Mathematics—a wonderful science, but it hasn't yet come up with a way to divide one tricycle among three little boys.

—Earl Wilson[4]

Building a Strong Foundation*

Young children delight in counting, matching, and looking for patterns. They learn basic mathematical concepts the way that they learned to walk and talk—with minimal interference from adults.

Then sometime in elementary school, many children learn to hate math. After a few sessions of "3 + 1 = 4, 3 + 2 = 5, 3 + 3...," they begin to whine. Older children recoil from long division. By the time they reach high school, students face torture like: *The product of an integer and the next greater integer is 20 less than the square of the greater integer.* Homework becomes a tedious chore to put off as long as possible or finish with slapdash speed.

Instead of drudgery, mathematics should be a game of discovery. It should give children the same *Aha! I've got it!* feeling they get from solving a challenging puzzle.

How can homeschool teachers help children retain their natural delight in math?

Back to basics

Math instruction suffers from a series of fads. Most of us remember the experiment with "New Math," which led to the reactionary "Back to Basics" movement. And I think everyone agrees that it is important for our children to master the basics of any subject they study.

---

* This chapter is condensed from **Aha! How To Teach Math So Kids Get It.**

But what is basic mathematics?

Is basic mathematics 2 + 2 = 4? Is it knowing the times tables by heart? Is it being able to pass a machine-scored, multiple-choice standardized achievement test?

No, no, and certainly not!

Math is a tool for problem solving. So learning basic mathematics means learning to solve problems. With basic mathematics, your children can think a situation through. They can find patterns, make mental connections between ideas, twist things and turn them and toss them around in their minds until they find a solution.

Children have this basic mathematical ability, and they delight in using it. As homeschool teachers, we need to help them build their problem-solving skills. And the best way to build these skills is through the challenge of puzzles and games.

Math the mathematician's way

What do real mathematicians, people who actually enjoy working with math, have to say about their subject? Edward Rothstein wrote, "Real mathematics is not just formulaic tutoring. My hope is that children learn to think about mathematics as a kind of mental play."[5]

And John Allen Paulos wrote in **Innumeracy**, a book detailing America's astounding math illiteracy: "If mathematics education communicated this playful aspect of the subject, I don't think innumeracy would be as widespread as it is."

Basic mathematics is mental play. This is the essence of creative problem solving. This is what we need to teach our children—more important than fractions or decimals or even the times tables. Math is not just rules and rote memory. Math is a game, playing with ideas.

Truly multicultural mathematics

Maybe we should try teaching math like the Japanese do, by challenging students to play around with difficult problems.

A comparison study of teaching styles found that Japanese math classes spent less than half the time that Americans spent practicing routine computation—and Japanese students took home almost no homework. Instead, they focused on one or two problems each class period.

The Japanese teacher would introduce a challenging problem, something near the edge of her class's mathematical ability. First, she would give them several minutes to work on the problem alone, to experiment with different ideas and toss options around in their heads or on paper. Only after the students played with the problem did the teacher come back and guide them toward a solution.

The researchers concluded, "The differences are not just a matter of degree: U.S. students apparently experience a different *kind* of mathematics than their Japanese peers."[6]

While American teachers drilled math facts, Japanese teachers taught their students to think, to explore mathematical concepts and play with ideas. Is it any wonder their students perform so well on international tests?

How to teach math as mental play

◆ Teach children to enjoy a challenge.

Give your children a good taste of that "Aha!" feeling. This attitude is easier caught than taught. You are their role model. Do you enjoy wrestling with puzzles and story problems? Treat yourself to a Brian Bolt, Martin Gardner, or Raymond Smullyan book from the library.

◆ Teach creative reasoning.

Play with tangrams and other visual perception toys. Use strategy games, puzzles, and brainteasers to force children out of their mental ruts. Mini-mystery books exercise the same thinking muscles.

◆ Teach mental math skills.

You can buy **Mental Math** workbooks, or simply go through your textbooks orally. Help your children learn to estimate, and they will be able to figure out many problems in their heads.

Playing around with the number line

What does it mean to teach math as mental play?

Many people think that teachers need to make math fun with flashy computer games or cartoon heroes. They don't realize that abstract mathematical ideas themselves can be as fun as any toys. Children enjoy playing around with concepts normally reserved for older students—for instance, negative numbers.

Negative numbers are easy for even young children to understand: Tape the number line to the wall vertically, with zero at table height. Extend your number line to include negatives, counting backwards from zero like the BC years on a time line. Zero is "ground level," and the negatives are in a hole.

Run your fingers up and down the number line as you add or subtract. But try not to call the negatives "minus" numbers—it's a bad habit, like saying "ain't."

Fiddle with the negative numbers in a no-stress, no-test way:

- How are they different from positive numbers? What happens if you add or subtract them?
  - ⇒ How strange! When you add a negative number, your total gets smaller.
- Can you multiply with negative numbers, or divide? Try it with numbers that fit on your fingers, to see the principles more clearly:
  - ⇒ 1×-1 has to be -1, since anything times one is itself.
  - ⇒ What is 2×-2? Think of starting at zero and counting -2 twice, to get -4.
- If your children figure out multiplication, let them try division. What is $-6 \div 2$?
  - ⇒ If you cut -6 in half, what would it be? That is not so hard: -3.
- Or what about double negatives, a no-no in grammar?
  - ⇒ $-(-1)$ = the opposite of -1 = $+1$
  - ⇒ $-(-(-1))$ = the opposite of (the opposite of -1)
= the opposite of $+1$ = -1
  - ⇒ In math, double negatives cancel each other out.

Despite that third grade teacher who told us we couldn't subtract six from four, negative numbers help clarify many real-life situations—winter temperatures, for example, or the bank account of someone who relies too much on credit cards.

But even if they weren't useful, it would be fun to play around with the idea of negative numbers, and to figure out how they work.

In the few years we have our children at home, we can't possibly teach them everything they will need as adults. At best, we can give them the tools to continue their own education. And one of the most important tools for learning is a solid understanding of real mathematics—math taught the mathematician's way, as mental play.

Textbook management tips

1. Use the textbook as a coach's manual.

The textbook is more for the teacher than for the student. You read the lesson, and your child answers orally. With elementary students, limit your sessions to half an hour, maybe two or three times a week.

2. Don't be afraid to skip and skim.

Use the review test at the end of each chapter as an oral pretest. If your child already knows the material, move on ahead. When you hit new or confusing material, slow down and take turns doing the problems.

3. Three problems he can explain make for better practice than 20 problems done by rote.

Have your child work a few problems and explain them back to you. If he gets something wrong, you will know what he doesn't understand—or whether he did understand the math but made a minor mistake (like forgetting to add in a carried digit).

4. Avoid teaching rules for solving the problems.

Rules are easy to mix up or forget. Instead, help him see *why* it works that way. Try working a similar but easier problem to demonstrate the principles more clearly, or use manipulatives if you find them helpful. Or give up. If an idea doesn't click after several tries, go on to something different. Then come back to the hard topic in a few months. Your child may surprise you by figuring it out on his own.

5. Don't make your child copy down the exercises if he can do them in his head.

I have my fifth-grader keep scratch paper handy, but she doesn't have to turn anything in. Mental calculation is a valuable skill.

6. When your child cannot do a problem in his head, teach him to use round numbers and estimate.

Estimating is another useful skill for everyday life. And using round numbers keeps him focused on the process of solving problems instead of the mechanics of long division.

Arithmetic is neither fish nor beast; therefore it must be foul.

—*Anonymous*[7]

Adding and Subtracting with the Teacher's Best Friend

Math games and puzzles are fine, but what about the real killers of arithmetic: factors, fractions, and long division? Nobody ever developed math anxiety from playing with tangrams.

What do we do with the math monsters?

Many homeschooling parents see their children struggling with math, so they decide to balance abstract textbook instruction with hands-on demonstrations. Geoboards, plastic teddy bears, fraction hamburgers—school supply catalogs are full of manipulatives. Some say a teacher's best weapons against math monsters are the colorful *Cuisenaire rods.* I tried the rods, but learning to use them took more time than my patience would allow. Also, to use the rods well you need a gaggle of workbooks covering various topics.

I prefer *base ten blocks,* which are easy to use for arithmetic through algebra.

Base ten basics

Base ten blocks help children visualize place value, borrowing, multiplication of large numbers, division, factors...and I know nothing else that can give your children a tangible picture of $x^2 + 3x + 2$.

A teaching tool that versatile for about the price of one textbook—who could resist?

When you shop for a set of base ten blocks, look for plastic or wooden blocks that do *not* hook together (the Lego-like bumps will get in the way when your child tries to line up blocks). Get the biggest set you can reasonably afford. If your children are young, you may want to start with a one-color set. For older children or larger families, consider Nasco's **Algebra Base Ten Set**, which has a second color for negative numbers and will carry you through high school.[8]

Avoid the cheap set of blocks in assorted colors for place value: blue hundreds, green tens, and yellow ones. The subliminal message is that tens are a different kind of number from ones, not just a different quantity. There *are* different kinds of numbers. Tenths and sixths are different—you can't add them together unless you change them first. Also, positive and negative numbers are different—when you subtract negative numbers, they make your answer larger. But tens and hundreds are the same kind of number. It's just that hundreds are bigger.

Whichever set of blocks you choose, I suggest buying Cuisenaire's two-book set, **Games and Activities with Base 10 Blocks**. (You can get by with just Book 2, if your children are older.) Work through the books yourself to gain a solid understanding of how the blocks work. Then share with your students the workbook pages you found helpful. Most of us need this experience before we can teach with base ten blocks, since we had nothing like them when we were in school.

Place value: Key to the modern world

Base ten blocks are designed to teach place value, the foundation of our base ten number system.

The idea of place value came relatively late in the history of mankind. King Tut, Plato, and Jesus never worked with numbers that changed their meaning depending on position. What a strange idea it would be to someone who only knew Egyptian or Roman numerals that the 2 in 24 means an entirely different quantity than the 2 in 42.[9]

Yes, the later Romans did change from addition to subtraction depending on position, so that IX is a different number from XI. Even so, the I always stood for one and the X for ten. But in 24 the 2 means 20, and in 42 the 2 *doesn't* mean 20.

Moreover, that change in meaning is the key to nearly all the advances of science. Without place value, we would not have the math to describe and understand electricity—so no TV's or refrigerators. We would not have been able to build a computer or send a man to the moon. Place value is a powerful problem-solving tool.

As one mathematician said, "The simplest schoolboy is now familiar with facts for which Archimedes would have sacrificed his life."[10]

Of course, children will not be doing rocket-science calculations in elementary school. Nevertheless, even the most basic math is easier when children truly understand place value.

Playing with place value

Introduce the base ten blocks as an easy way to keep score in a favorite game. Ideally, use a game that your child enjoys and in which scores can rise to 100 or more.

If you don't have a favorite game, try ***Math Dice***:

- Using a set of five Yahtzee dice, throw three times, aiming for the highest possible score.
- With each throw, your child can set aside as many dice as he wants to keep.
- But at the end of the third throw, what he sees is what he gets for that turn.
- The first player to reach 100 wins the game. For a longer game, play to 300.

Let your child be the banker, counting out one unit block for each point earned. He will quickly realize that it is easier to count a ten rod than ten individual ones and that a score of 12 means a rod and two ones.

These are the first steps toward a solid understanding of place value.

If you can help it, do not point out these things yourself. Let him discover them—he will understand better and remember the ideas when he thinks of them himself. If he wants to count the blocks one by one, let him. Eventually he will run out of individual blocks. Then, when he is stuck, he will be forced to think of another way to do it.

> Most people fail to understand the importance of *stuckness* to creative thinking, whether they are solving a math problem or writing a novel. Only when children are stuck are they forced to do the hard mental work of *figuring it out.*
>
> When your child is stuck on a problem, whether with blocks or on paper, that is a good time for you to go fix a cup of coffee. It is hard to stay in the same room without offering advice, but if you give an answer too soon, you rob your child of the opportunity to feel that *"Aha!"* thrill.

Base ten tips

1. Always have young children match blocks when making change, to make sure the trade is fair. To change 10 ones into a ten rod, line up the small blocks along the side of the rod until you have the right amount. It is so easy for children to miscount, and wrong answers discourage young thinkers.

2. The hundred block is called a *flat.* To trade 10 rods for a flat, have your child lay the rods on top of the flat to make sure he has the right number. Matching the blocks will eliminate counting errors.

The place value sorting chart

The real trick comes when the game is over. Perhaps one player collected a pile of 7 rods and 43 ones, another child earned a hundred flat and 3 rods, and the last person stacked up 11 rods and 15 ones. If Christine simply compares piles of blocks, she may think the first player's pile looks largest. A pile of ten unit blocks seems like more than one rod, because the loose blocks spread out over more of the table. However, the second player has the biggest piece.

Who won?

To compare the blocks, I help Christine make a place value chart. If we draw it on a sheet of construction paper and laminate it, the chart will last through several months' worth of games. But the nice thing about a chart like this is that it's so easy, your child can whip one out whenever he needs it.

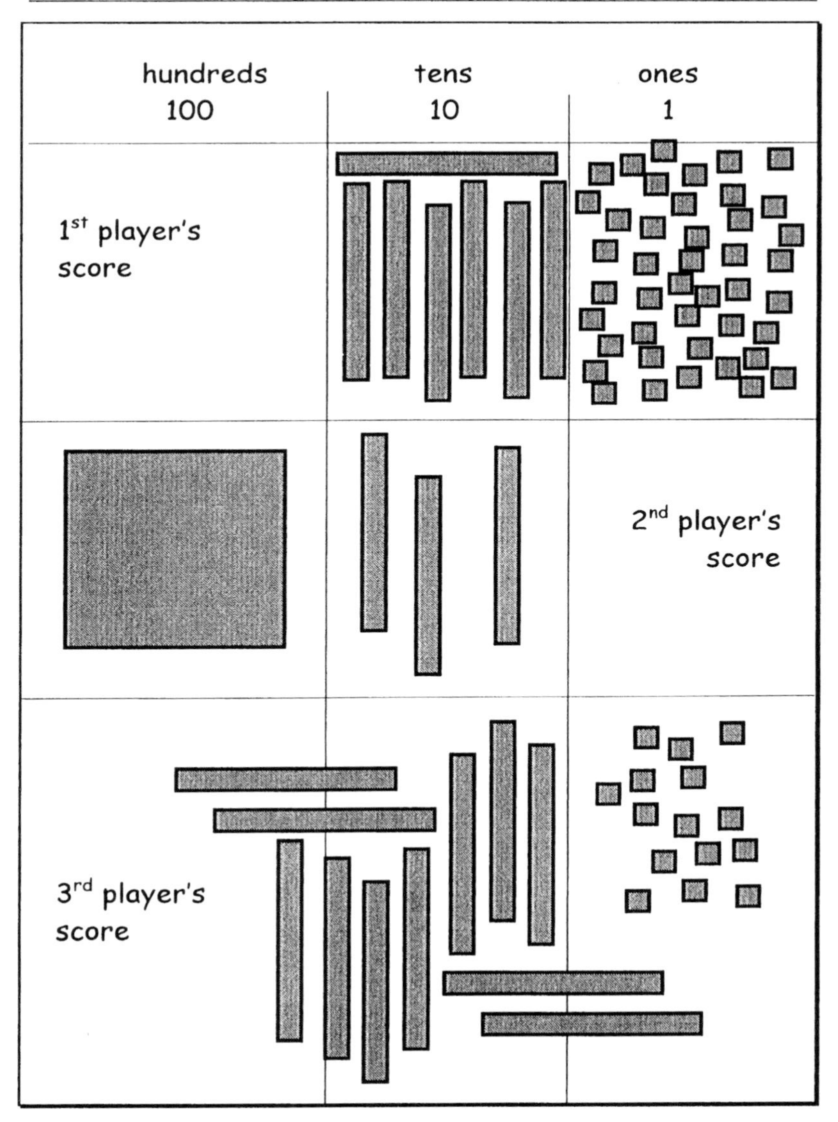

After sorting the blocks into the proper columns, Christine may still find it difficult to tell who has the most points. That pile of 43 ones looks awfully big. There is *nothing wrong* with having double digits in any given column. Those 43 ones are fine where they are, or she can trade them for 4 ten rods and 3 ones. They add up to the same score either way—but the rods are easier to compare at a glance.

This flexibility of the place value system is important for children to understand, especially when dealing with large numbers. For example, Christine's older sister Deborah works problems like 693 x 27 = ? She has to keep the place value straight as she calculates (7 x 693) ones and (2 x 693) tens.

Even though 43 ones are okay, Christine eventually needs to learn how to trade them in and to trade the third player's rods for a 100 flat. This makes fewer pieces, so they are easier to work with. Then she will be able to see at a glance which score is larger.

So if she doesn't think of it herself, I will prompt her: "Is there any way we can make it easier to compare the scores?"

Whether I have Christine add up the blocks and write down a total score depends on her level of understanding. Counting, playing with the numbers in her head, sorting M & M's, sharing cookies with her brothers, and trading in blocks to make change—all of these things build *number sense.* Number sense is the understanding of what the numbers really mean.

> Until a child has a firm grasp on number sense,
> having him write the digits
> is an exercise in penmanship,
> not math.

I probably would have Christine write the totals. She can count past 100 and can usually solve oral story problems involving simple fractions or negative numbers. She enjoys writing out single-digit addition or subtraction problems when she and Deborah play school. And she can even solve simple algebraic equations, when I remind her that *x* means a mystery number. All this tells me her number sense is well developed, even though she sometimes forgets that "33" means "three tens and three more."

(The Roman system, where writing the number twice means you have two of them so that "33" would mean "*three* and three more, or six," seems more natural to her. We don't slave over place value, but whenever we see a two-digit number I remind her what it means.)

More place value practice

There is another base ten manipulative children love to play with—money. Use pennies for ones, dimes for tens, and dollars for hundreds. Pretend money will work, but it doesn't have the same motivating magic as the real thing.

Even so, I do not recommend money as your main tool for teaching place value. Dimes look different from pennies, but in our base ten system, tens are not different from ones, except that they are bigger. Base ten blocks make the 1 + 1 + 1 + ... = 10 relationship intuitively clear.

Introducing double-digit addition

The place value sorting chart also makes for an easy transition to double-digit addition. Children can set up each number's tens and ones in the proper columns, then push the piles together to add them. To get the final answer, trade in any extra blocks until there is only one digit in each column.

So if my daughter Christine wanted to add 24 + 58, she would count out 2 rods and 4 unit blocks and set them on the chart. Then she would lay down 5 rods and 8 ones for the next number. Pushing the piles together gives 7 rods and 12 ones. Finally, she trades in 10 ones for another rod: 24 + 58 = 82.

Of course, Christine would not have to use the place value chart to add two numbers. Piles on the table would work just as well. But using the chart reinforces the idea of working in columns.

I want Christine to think *automatically* of lining up numbers in columns. This will—I hope—keep her from getting confused when she moves on to multiplication and long division.

```
 24
+58
 12 ones
+7  tens
 82
```

When Christine is ready to add without the blocks, I won't teach carrying right away. Instead, I will show her how to add the numbers in the ones column and the numbers in the tens column, just like with the blocks. Then she can add those sums together to get her total answer.

I'll wait to see if she will invent the idea of carrying on her own. If she is like her older siblings, she should be an expert at discovering new shortcuts.

Watch those columns!

Working in columns is the key to doing calculations in our base ten number system. Keep reminding your children that the columns stand for hundreds and tens and ones.

You can tell your children to put in the zeros to show this: Christine might write "70" instead of "7" in the problem above. This zero works as a space-holder, keeping those 7 tens lined up where they belong. Or she might draw lines to separate the columns, like a mini version of the place value chart.

But my kids are lazy enough to resent writing extra lines or zeros. That is okay, as long as they *think* in columns.

Or try it this way

When you look at math as mental play, there is usually more than one way to solve any problem.

Children do not have to add the ones column first. Many people find it more natural to work from left to right, the way we read a book. Moreover, working with the big numbers first is important in estimating, which is a valuable tool for solving practical problems. If Deborah wants to buy a $5.95 toy and a book for $11.50, she doesn't have to add the pennies to know that a $20 bill is enough.

```
  24
+58
   7 tens
+12 ones
  82
```

Or, to solve a problem in one step, adjust the subtotal as you go along....

```
 724
+158
  8̶7̶
 882
```

Working left to right, children can cross out digits or adjust their subtotal in their heads. Encourage your student to try solving addition problems both ways before deciding which way he likes best.

Subtraction without borrowing

Remember that third grade teacher who said you could not subtract 6 from 4?

Well, that is exactly what your child is going to do.

Working in place value columns is the key to subtraction without borrowing. Just as with the addition problem above, your child will subtract the ones column and the tens column and then add those two numbers together to get his final answer.

The trick is that sometimes he will end up with a negative number in one of the columns. That is child's play for anyone who has ever solved problems on a number line. To solve 4 – 6, just start at 4 and count down 6 spaces, which brings you to -2. (See page 11 for more about solving problems with negative numbers.)

In the problem at right, 54 – 46 leaves you with one ten and -2 ones. And of course, -2 + 10 make a total of 8.

```
  54
- 46
  -2 ones
+  1 tens
   8
```

Children may also work subtraction from left to right. This has the same advantages as in addition problems: It feels more natural to many people who learned to read from left to right, and it focuses on the biggest numbers first. If your child is estimating an answer, he can work only the columns he needs.

```
 354
-176
   2  hundreds
  -2  tens
+ -2  ones
  18  tens
+ -2  ones
 178  final answer
```

Or, to work it in one step, adjusting as you go...

 354
−176
~~2~~
~~18~~
178

Let your children try working problems both ways. Even if they decide that traditional borrowing is easier, they will gain insight by the experiment.

Number base 8
is just like number base 10, really...
if you're missing two fingers.

—Tom Lehrer[11]

***

Numbers written in base 8
are called octal numbers,
while base 10 numbers are called decimals.

In base 8,
the place value columns are
ones, eights, sixty-fourths, etc.
So 31 octal
means 3 eights and 1 one,
which is 25 decimal:

31 OCT = 25 DEC

Does this mean that
Halloween and Christmas
fall on the same day of the year?

—Anonymous[12]

There is nothing that is so troublesome to mathematical practice, nor that doth more molest and hinder calculators, than the multiplications...of great numbers, which besides the tedious expense of time are for the most part subject to many slippery errors...

—*John Napier*[13]

Multiplication: Rectangle Mania

Give your students a head start on higher math by lining up base ten blocks in rectangles. Count the ***over*** and ***up*** dimensions. Find the ***area***—the total number of blocks. Take as much time as you need to make sure your children understand these concepts.

Over, *up*, and *area* are the keys to understanding multiplication and division with base ten blocks.

Notice that you can make different rectangles with the same area. Twelve is a good number to demonstrate this. Your children can build two over by six up (2 x 6) or three over by four up (3 x 4). Don't forget that 1 x 12 is also a rectangle, though a strange-looking one.

Try other numbers. Which numbers make squares? Can your student guess what we call these numbers? Which numbers only make lines?[14]

Factoring with rectangles

Have older children use graph paper to draw a chart of all the rectangles they can make with different groups of blocks, starting at one and adding one block at a time.

One, two, and three will have only one rectangle each. But with four blocks we can make a 1 x 4 rectangle or a 2 x 2 square. With 48 blocks we can make five different rectangles: 1 x 48, 2 x 24, 3 x 16, 4 x 12, and 6 x 8. Can you find a number less than 48 that makes five rectangles? Can you find a number less than 100 that makes more than five?

[I found four numbers less than 100 that could make more than five rectangles. See the answers to this and other sample problems throughout the book in the appendix, page 91.]

There is a math term for what we just did: *factoring*.

When we made all the different rectangles we could with 48 blocks, we were finding the *factors* of 48—all the whole numbers that can be multiplied by something to get that number. The factors of 48 are the sides of the different rectangles: 1, 2, 3, 4, 6, 8, 12, 16, 24, and 48. And 48 is a *multiple* of each of its factors.

Factors are useful to know for simplifying fractions. Recognizing factors will make it easy to put a fraction in lowest terms or to find the lowest common denominator of two fractions. And factoring will come up again in algebra, for solving polynomial equations.

Nevertheless, do not make your children memorize the factors of 48 or any other number. Simply have them make the chart and look for patterns, then discuss the term *factor* as a vocabulary word. Try to use the word several times, so your children will recognize what it means the next time they stumble over it in a textbook.

If kids understand the concept of factoring, they will be able to find whatever factors they need when the time comes to use them.

How to visualize multiplication

There are three basic ways children can picture what happens when they multiply. Teach all three to give your children a well-rounded understanding of arithmetic:

1. Groups

Think of four plates with three cookies on each plate (4 x 3 = 12 cookies), or five baskets of 12 apples each (5 x 12 = 60 apples), or two bags with a marble in each one (2 x 1 = 2 marbles). This is the easiest way to understand multiplication, and it works for many simple problems.

2. Skip counting

This means counting by twos or fives or tens. You can also imagine skip counting as repeated jumps on a number line. This is perhaps the most abstract way to multiply, but that also makes it one of the quickest. If you can't remember what 5 x 7 equals, it's easy to count seven fives: 5, 10, 15, 20, 25, 30, 35. (I use my fingers to keep track of how many fives I have counted. Useful things, fingers.)

3. Rectangles (or Area)

Imagine measuring carpet, planting a garden, or estimating how many gallons of paint it will take to cover a wall. Rectangles are flexible, useful, real-life models of multiplication, but most teachers avoid them. Groups are so easy for children and teachers alike that rectangles are often ignored.

Rectangles are basic to much of algebra, geometry, and calculus, as well as being important in everyday math problems. Groups and skip counting are fine for young children, but please make sure that your fifth- or sixth-graders get plenty of practice with rectangles as well.

Multiplication Rummy

This game helps children remember the multiplication pictures, so it builds understanding even for those who know their math facts. Play it as a family.

Cut card stock into playing-card-sized pieces. For each fact you want to practice, make four cards—one "book":

1. The multiplication equation (3 x 4 = 12)
2. Plates of cookies (3 circles with 4 dots in each)
3. Jumps on the number line (3 jumps of 4 spaces)
4. A rectangle (3 squares by 4 squares)

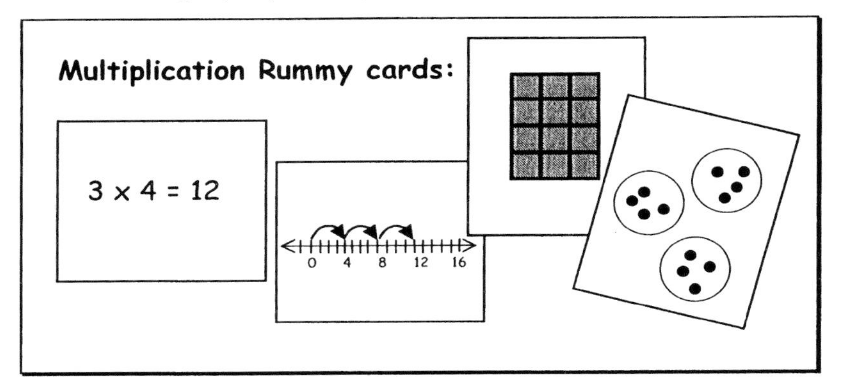

Have your children help make the cards. A well-balanced card deck might include parts of the three, four, five, six, and seven times tables. (With eight and nine, the number line cards get crowded.) Be careful not to make duplicate cards—3 x 4 is the same as 4 x 3.

To play, deal ten cards to each player. Turn up the top card from the stack to start the discard pile.

On his turn, each player may either draw from the stack or pick up the discard pile as far back as desired. But if he picks up more than the top discard, he has to meld the farthest-back card he picks up. When a player collects at least three cards in a book, he may meld (lay them down). If he has the fourth card in a book that is already on the table, he may lay that down, too. Then the player discards to end his turn.

Play continues clockwise around the table until one player runs out of cards. (A discard is optional when going out.) Then count the score as follows:

- Every card on the table is worth +5 points.
- Every card in the hand is worth −2 points.
- The player who went out gains a bonus of +15 points.

You may play a single hand, just for fun. Or play several hands, and the first player to reach 300 points wins.

Hands-on multiplication

Multiplication is a cinch with base ten blocks: 3 x 4 means three *over* by four *up*, or three groups of four. If you have four rows of three blocks each, how many blocks do you have? The *area* gives the answer: 12 blocks. To multiply any two numbers, simply build a rectangle with sides the size of the numbers. Then to get the answer, count how many blocks that took

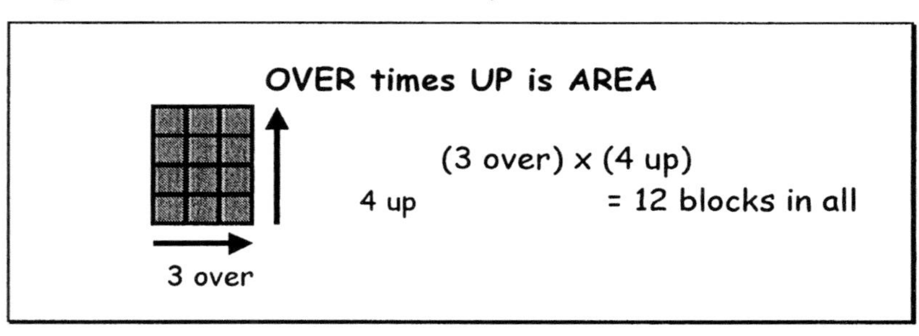

A first-grader can do this, and will boast that she is doing the same schoolwork her older brother does. Keep it playful, and math might become her favorite subject.

Of course, most children can picture three groups of four in their heads, without shuffling blocks. If they have played with oral story problems, they may have solved problems like that in kindergarten. But what about the messy problems they will find in a fourth- or fifth-grade textbook, which require multiplying partial products and keeping the numbers lined up right, so they don't mix the tens and the ones?

What about, say, 16 x 23? A first-grader can't work that in her head, but her fourth-grade sister will be able to—after she learns to use base ten blocks.

Over times up is area. Here is how it works: Deborah grabs a pile of blocks and starts to build her *over* dimension. Since the up and over dimensions are both greater than 10, she can start with a hundred flat (10 x 10). To make the 16 over she lays out six rods along the right side of her hundred.

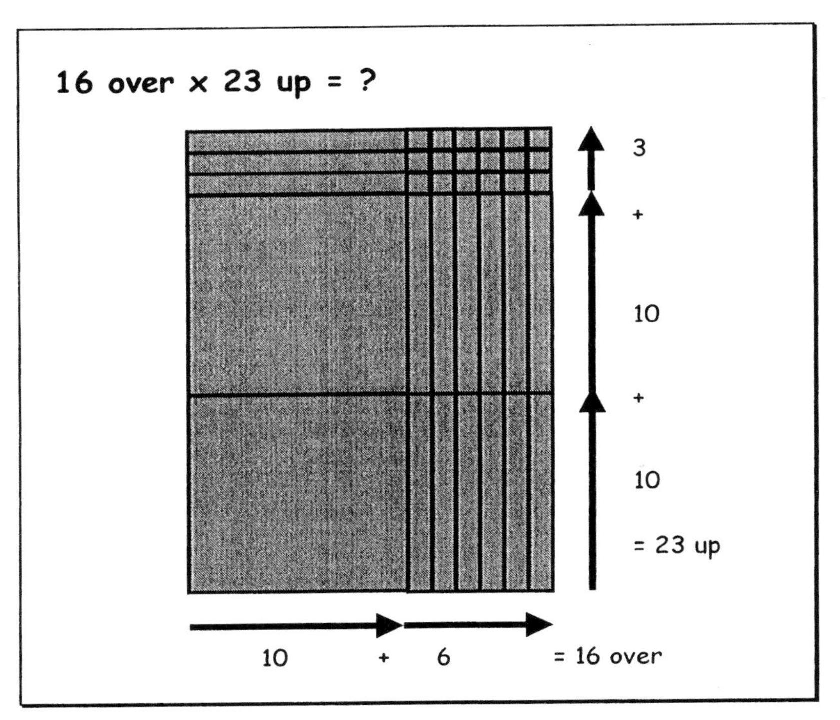

Now for the *up* dimension. She adds a second hundred flat, with six more ten rods alongside it (keeping her 16 over dimension). This brings her to 20 up, and three rods across the top makes 23.

But she still doesn't have a rectangle. She fills in the top right-hand corner with unit blocks.

Got it! A rectangle of 16 x 23, and all she has to do is count the blocks to get her answer: two hundreds, 15 ten rods, and 18 ones.

To put the number in standard form, she will need to trade in some blocks: 10 ones make another rod, and 10 rods make a flat, so 16 x 23 = 368.

Working with the blocks is hands-on fun, for awhile, but Deborah's natural laziness will push her to abstraction. It will not be long before she looks at a problem and imagines those blocks in her mind: "I don't have to build it, Mom. It's too easy."

Partial products: Multiplying on paper

Solving base ten block problems in one's head is easy, as long as the numbers stay relatively small. But what about older brother Jonathan's seventh-grade book, with its monster multiplication problems like 7569 x 384 = ?

Use base ten blocks to make the transition to pencil and paper math in a tangible, hands-on way—with *partial products.* A partial product is one *part* of a multiplication problem, small enough to work in your head.

Children who are used to working addition and subtraction problems in columns should have no trouble applying that concept to multiplication.

$$16 \times 23 = (1 \text{ ten} + 6 \text{ ones}) \times 23$$
$$= (1 \times 23) \text{ tens} + (6 \times 23) \text{ ones}$$

Imagine Deborah's 16 x 23 rectangle, split vertically between the hundred blocks and the ten rods. This cuts the big problem into two smaller parts. On the right, the rods and the unit blocks above them make (6 x 23) ones. The column on the left is (1 x 23) tens. The columns can be split again to eliminate carrying, if desired.

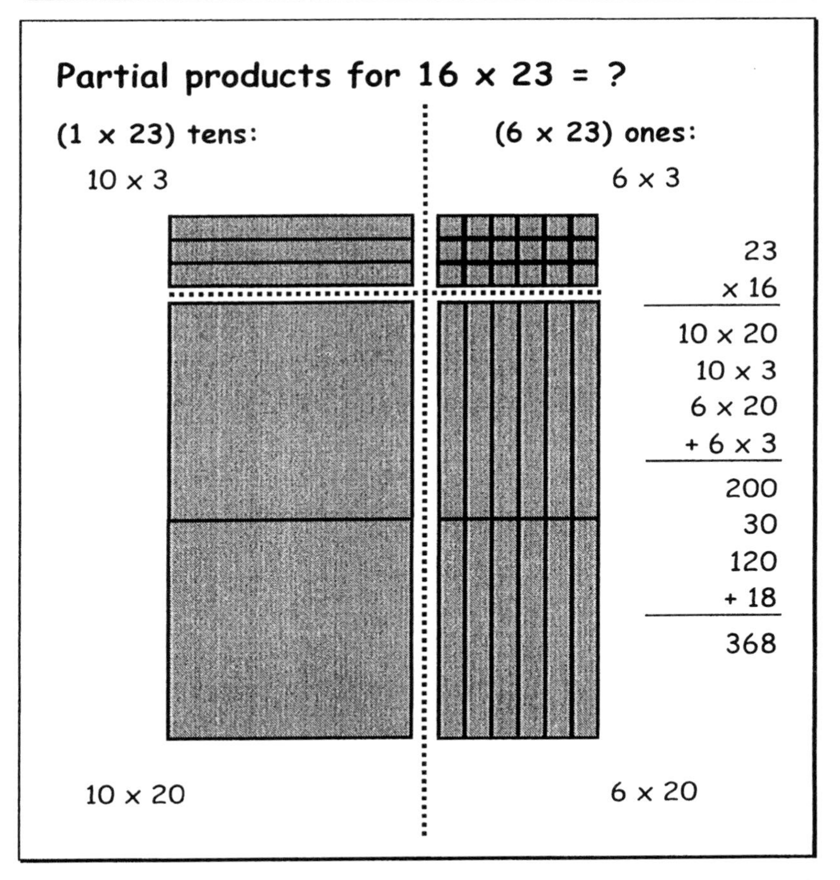

Have your children identify the partial products in several multiplication rectangles and show how these parts go together to make the final answer. If children thoroughly understand each of these steps, they are less likely to get their ones and tens columns tangled when working big problems.

Again, multiplication problems may be worked either from left to right or in the traditional method, from right to left.

If your children like to draw column lines or to use zeros as spacers, that is fine. My children don't like to write anything they don't have to. As long as they keep the tens and hundreds straight—as long as they *think* in columns—I let them write it however they like.

Just *keep those columns lined up!*

Perhaps I could best describe
my experience of doing mathematics
in terms of entering a dark mansion.

One goes into the first room
and it's dark,
completely dark.
One stumbles around
bumping into the furniture
and then gradually
you learn where each piece of furniture is.

And finally after six months or so
you find the light switch,
you turn it on.
Suddenly it's all illuminated,
you can see exactly where you were.

—Andrew Wiles[15]

He who can properly define and divide is considered to be a god.

—*Plato*[16]

The Dragons of Long Division

The trouble with textbook division problems is not the concept of division. Preschool children understand the basic idea of division: sharing a plate of cookies. The trouble is the sheer volume of stuff the student has to split up.

Who ever heard of dividing 496 cookies between four people?

The easiest way to approach division is to think of it as *backwards multiplication.* That is, $12 \div 4$ means: If we have twelve cookies to split between four people, how many cookies will each person get?

Or to put it in other words, *what* times 4 equals 12?

Division is multiplication done backwards

For most people—certainly for most children—multiplication is much easier than division. Often, all it takes to solve a division problem is to change it into multiplication.

$$12 \div 4 \text{ means } \square \times 4 = 12$$

and

$$39 \div 3 \text{ means } \square \times 3 = 39$$

Try this method on two-digit division problems, too. You might be surprised how much you can do in your head.

$$75 \div 15 = \square ?$$

This is the same problem as $\square \times 15 = 75$.

Well, two 15's make 30, so four of them would be 60. One more 15 will do it:

$$5 \times 15 = 75$$

...and going back to the original problem:

$$75 \div 15 = 5$$

Let's try one more example, even harder.

$$432 \div 24 = \square ?$$

This becomes the multiplication problem:

$$\square \times 24 = 432$$

Ten 24's are 240, and twenty of them would be 480. That's too much, so the answer has to be less than 20. But how much less? Well, 480 – 432 = 48, which is two 24's. That gives me:

$$(20 - 2) \times 24 = 432$$

...and going back to the original problem...

$$432 \div 24 = 18$$

This trick always works, because it is based on the very definition of division. The more your student does his division homework using this method, the more thoroughly he will understand what division really means.

How many groups?

When we talk about a division problem, we commonly use the question, "How many?"

"How many 4's in 12?"

or

"How many 15's in 75?"

These "How many?" questions use the idea of groups—one of our multiplication pictures—as a way to understand division.

If you buy a tray of 12 bedding plants, and you want to set them out in groups of four, how many groups can you make? Or if you buy 75 bulbs, and you want to plant them in drifts of 15 because lonely daffodils always look sad, how many bunches of flowers will that be?

Division is multiplication done backwards.

Hands-on division

Base ten blocks can also help children make the mental connection between multiplication and division. Division is like a multiplication problem in which your child knows the answer and one of the factors and has to find the other factor.

Remember that factoring means making rectangles. In multiplication problems, your child knows the sides of his rectangle and calculates the area. In division, he knows the area and one side. He has to find the length of the other side.

Division with base ten blocks is easy. To calculate 12 ÷ 4, your child would take 12 blocks (area) and build a rectangle that is 4 up. The over dimension gives the answer.

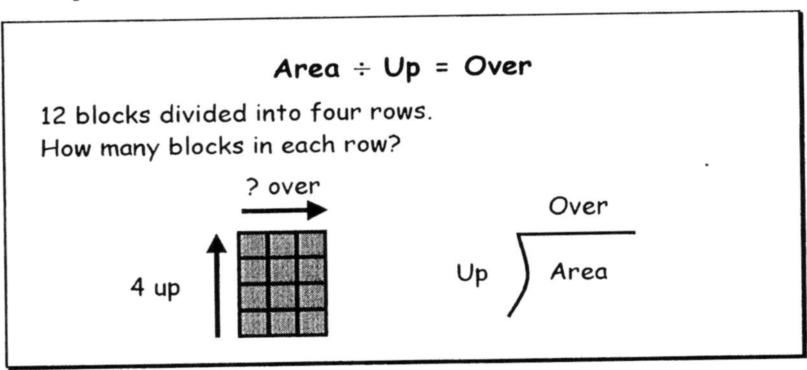

In the same way, 75 ÷ 15 means 75 blocks, made into a 15-by-something rectangle. If we make 15 rows of blocks, how many blocks will there be in each row?

To help your child remember, try this: The long division symbol looks a little bit like a rectangle with *up* on the left, *over* on top, and the *area* inside.

For example, Deborah might need to solve a problem like 104 ÷ 8 = ? Her first step is to think of it as a multiplication problem: *What* times 8 is 104?

She picks out 104 blocks for the area—a hundred flat and four ones. She will need to fit these blocks into a rectangle that is eight up. That will divide her area into eight rows of blocks. Then she can count how far over the blocks go, the number of blocks in each row, which will be her answer.

She notices right away the hundred is too high. It is 10 up, but she only needs 8, so she trades the hundred for 10 ten rods.

Deborah's problem: 104 area ÷ 8 up = ?

1. Count out the area, 104 blocks.

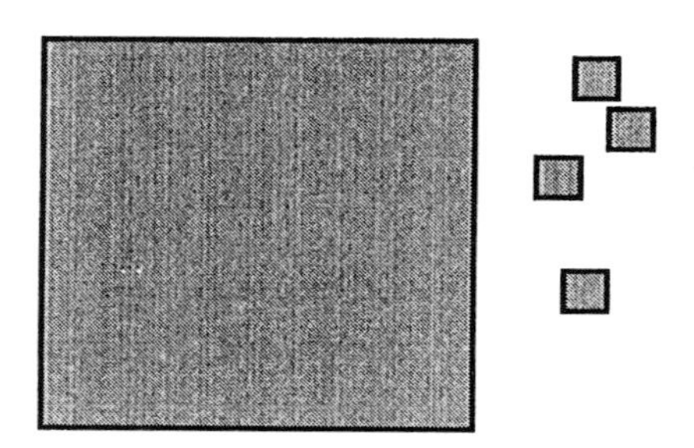

2. To divide by 8, make a rectangle that is 8 up.
(First, trade the 100 for 10 tens.)

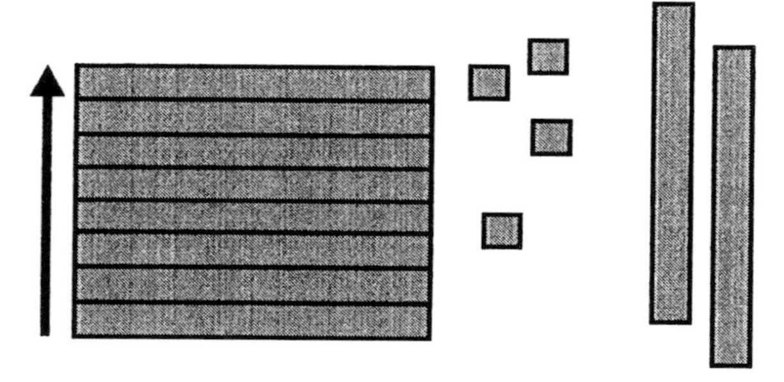

3. Count the over dimension for your answer.
104 blocks ÷ 8 rows = 13 blocks per row

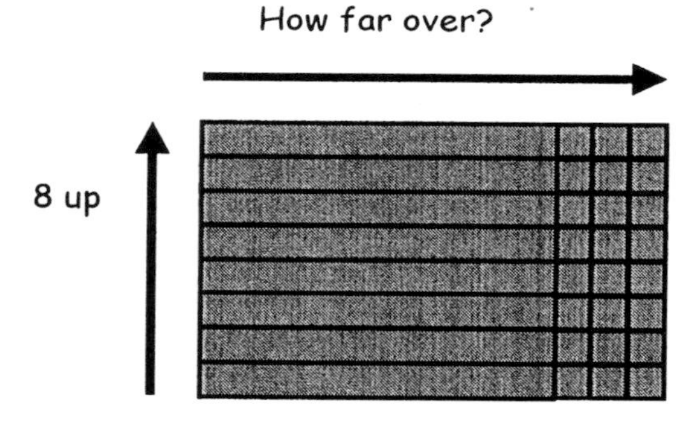

She can lay eight of these on their sides, for a rectangle 8 up by 10 over. Now she keeps building over until she runs out of blocks. She has two rods left, which she trades for 20 ones. Then she uses all her unit blocks to fill in the rectangle, for a total of 13 over: $104 \div 8 = 13$.

⇒ If you understood that, try this one yourself: $396 \div 18 = ?$

Long division monsters

But what about the real dragons of long division, problems like $9573 \div 26 = ?$ We don't have 9000 blocks, and few children can work through a problem like that on paper without getting their place value columns confused or their borrowing snarled.

Think about how people use math in real life. If I needed an exact answer to $9573 \div 26$, I would not trust myself to figure it out. Mistakes are far too easy to make. I would use a calculator. Wouldn't you?

If an approximate answer was enough, I could round off the numbers and figure it out in my head: almost 10,000 divided by about 25 gives me an estimate of 400. Since I rounded up, I know the real answer would be a little less.

Of course, children don't have the freedom of adults until they have passed at least a few standardized tests. But many tests allow calculators, and even those that don't will have only a few dragons on them. Is the cost in time and trouble to practice hundreds of these problems worth it, for such a limited benefit?

Why study long division?

Consider the standard arguments for teaching long division:

1. **"Long division teaches children to think."**
   Very few of the students I have taught could explain what they are doing in long division. They simply followed the teacher's recipe.

2. **"Long division teaches children to follow instructions."**
   So does baking—and baking rewards them if they do it right.

3. **"Long division reinforces the multiplication tables."**
   Yes, it does. So does a good math drill game, which is a lot more fun.

Long division was not invented merely to torture school children. It really is the easiest way to handle division with large numbers, *if* you have to do it by hand.

Children who have a solid understanding of place value and of what division means—and who write neatly enough to keep their columns straight—should have little trouble with long division. Deborah even considers long division fun, to the continual amazement of her older brother.

But if long division is a problem for your child, making him practice the recipe will do nothing to improve his understanding. Instead, teach him to round off the numbers and estimate his answer. When a student learns to estimate, he can focus on the meaning of the problem instead of worrying about the decimal point. If he needs an exact number, then he can use the calculator.

If children understand the basic idea of division, which is multiplication done backwards, they should do fine. Teach the techniques of long division with simple problems like 496 ÷ 4, do two or three harder ones for practice, and then spend the rest of the afternoon doing something really useful—like playing strategy games.

Remind your child that it is dangerous
to use a calculator
without first estimating his answer.

Hitting a wrong button
can cause unnoticed errors.

How it works: Watch those columns!

Think of division as sharing. Let's go back to the problem of dividing 496 cookies between 4 people—a sure prescription for a tummy ache.

No wonder everyone hates long division!

Work the problem from left to right, in columns, sharing out the big numbers first. When you're splitting up such a huge pile of stuff, you want to get the big things out of the way as soon as you can. You can worry about the little bits later.

$$496 \div 4 = (400 + 90 + 6) \div 4$$

You have four packages with 100 cookies in each package. Hand those our first, one to each of your four people. Next you have nine packages of 10 cookies each. Each person gets two packages. Finally, you share out the ones. Break open that last package of 10 cookies and add it to the six loose cookies you already had. Split those between your four people. How many will each person get?

$$496 \div 4 = 1 \text{ hundred} + 2 \text{ tens} + 4 \text{ ones} = 124 \text{ cookies}$$

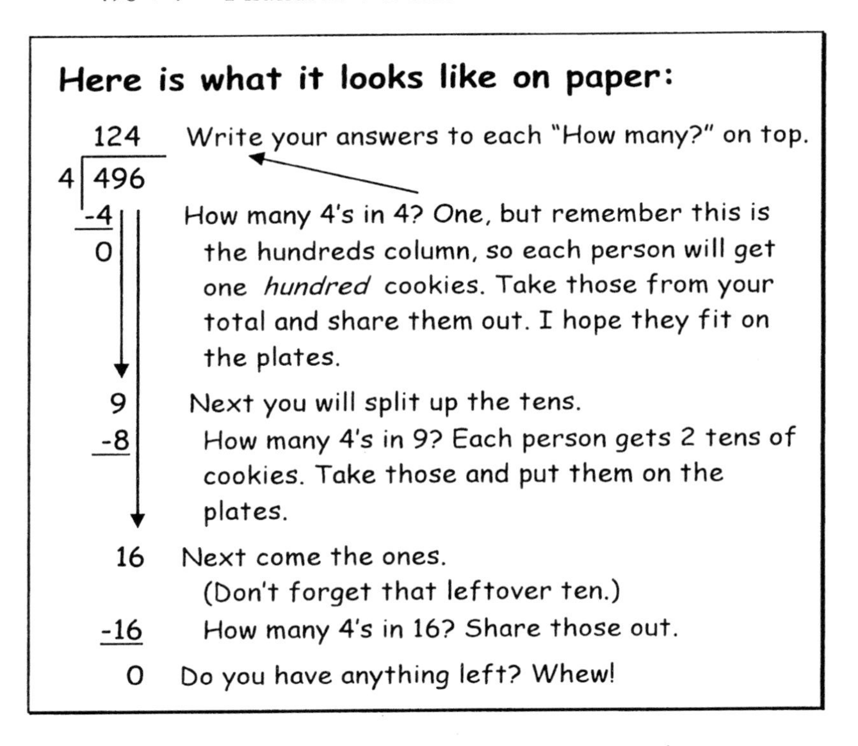

The method is the same with a bigger divisor—that is, more people. You can divide the cookies between 8, 12, or 37 people. Just start with the hundreds, share them out, and keep going until you run out of cookies.

One trick that helps many children is to write out a counting-by list in the margin of their paper. If Deborah has to divide by 12, she would write 12, 24, 36, 48, 60...up to 12 x 9 = 108. Then she can see at a glance how many 12's in whatever.

To divide 496 cookies between 12 people:

- How many 12's in 4 (hundreds)?
  None.
- How many 12's in 49 (tens)?
  Let's see: 12, 24, 36, 48. There are four 12's in 49 (tens). So the 12 people get 4 tens of cookies each, with one ten left over. Share them out.
- How many 12's in 16 ones (including that leftover ten)?
  Well, there is one 12, with four cookies left over.

So you can see that $496 \div 12 = 41$, with a remainder of four.

And the remainder is —?

How can we divide up those leftover cookies?

Think back to Deborah's base ten block problem on page 36. She built a rectangle for $104 \div 8 = 13$, but if she had started with 105 blocks, she would have one block that would not fit in her rectangle.

Imagine cutting that extra block into eight thin slices and making a fractional column, 8 up by $\frac{1}{8}$ over. Two blocks remaining would make two fractional columns, or $\frac{2}{8}$, three leftovers would make $\frac{3}{8}$, and so forth.

Remainders turn into fractions.

In $496 \div 12$, the leftover cookies make $\frac{4}{12} = \frac{1}{3}$ cookie per person.

I suppose you are two fathoms deep in mathematics, and if you are, then God help you. For so am I, only with this difference: I stick fast in the mud at the bottom, and there I shall remain.

—Charles Darwin[17]

Those Frustrating Fractions

Fractions confuse almost everybody. In fact, fractions probably cause more math phobia among children than any other topic in elementary school. Standardized tests are stacked with fraction questions, although many children find fractions impossible to understand. Fractions are a filter, separating the math "haves" from the luckless "have nots."

Mastering the rules

One big problem with fractions is that the rules do not seem to make sense. Can you explain these to your children? Start with an easy one...

1. If you need a common denominator to add or subtract fractions, why don't you need a common denominator when you multiply?

2. When you multiply both terms (the numerator and denominator) of a fraction by the same number, you get an equivalent fraction.

$$\frac{2}{3} = \frac{2 \times 4}{3 \times 4} = \frac{8}{12}$$

   When you divide both terms by the same number, you get an equivalent fraction.

$$\frac{3}{9} = \frac{3 \div 3}{9 \div 3} = \frac{1}{3}$$

Then when you add the same number to both terms, why don't you get an equivalent fraction?

$$\frac{1}{2}=\frac{1+1}{2+1}=\frac{2}{3} \text{ ? No!}$$

3. To multiply two fractions, you multiply the numerators and multiply the denominators.

$$\frac{1}{2}\times\frac{3}{5}=\frac{1\times 3}{2\times 5}=\frac{3}{10}$$

To divide fractions, can you divide the numerators and divide the denominators?

$$\frac{3}{4}\div\frac{1}{4}=\frac{3\div 1}{4\div 4}=\frac{3}{1}=3 \text{ ? Yes...}$$

...but it works only if you are careful to keep all the numbers in the right order. Remember that $3 \div 1 \neq 1 \div 3$.

Then, when you need to add fractions, why can't you just add the numerators and add the denominators?

$$\frac{1}{4}+\frac{1}{4}=\frac{1+1}{4+4}=\frac{2}{8} \text{ ? NO!}$$

4. When you divide by a fraction, you can flip the fraction over and multiply.

$$4\div\frac{1}{2}=4\times\frac{2}{1}=8$$

When you multiply by a fraction, can you flip the fraction over and divide?

$$4\times\frac{1}{2}=4\div\frac{2}{1}=2 \text{ ? Yes, it works.}$$

Then, when you have to subtract a fraction, why can't you just flip it over and add?

5. If you divide by flipping the fraction over and multiplying, does it matter which fraction you flip?

$$\frac{2}{3}\div\frac{1}{3}=\frac{2}{3}\times\frac{3}{1}=2$$

But if I flipped the other fraction:

$$\frac{2}{3} \div \frac{1}{3} = \frac{3}{2} \times \frac{1}{3} = \frac{1}{2} \text{ ? NO!!}$$

Only the first equation is correct, so it definitely matters which fraction you flip. *Why* does it matter?

How shall we then teach?

With so many apparent inconsistencies, you can see why children (and their teachers) get confused. And yet, fractions are vital to our children's test scores—and scores are important to college admissions officers. What is a teacher to do? Can anyone make sense out of this?

Must we tell our children, "Do it this way, and don't ask questions"?

Upper-elementary textbooks devote a tremendous number of pages to teaching fractions, and still students struggle. I wonder if all this is necessary. How often do you multiply fractions in your adult life? Except for baking a double recipe of cookies, I would bet it's not often.

If my 5th-grade daughter understands what a fraction is and how to use it in real-life situations, that is enough for now. She may not get every question right on a standardized test, but she will do okay.

Remember that tests are not real mathematics. Real, basic mathematics means learning to solve problems.

What elementary students need to know about fractions:

How to read a fraction.

How to work with fraction families.

"Of" means multiply.

In junior high, add three more ideas:

A fraction is a division problem.

A fraction is a comparison.

A fraction is a reciprocal.

How to read a fraction

The first confusing thing about fractions is vocabulary: those awful words *numerator* and *denominator.* To keep them straight, learn how to read a fraction.

Teach your children to read fractions from top to bottom, like pages in a book. The top number of a fraction is its first name, which tells how many pieces you have. The line in a fraction means *divided by,* so $3/4 = 3 \div 4$ and $5 \div 2 = 5/2$. And the bottom number is the fraction's last name or family name. It tells what size the pieces are.

Now, let's go through that a little slower.

First name = how many	
———————————	*(divided by)*
Last name = what size	

➢ *Numerator: the fraction's first name*

The top number in a fraction is its first name—that is, the first thing you hear about the fraction. A fraction's first name counts the number of pieces: $2/4$ has two pieces, and $3/4$ has three of them. Think *number* to help you remember the word numerator.

This makes it easy to count total number of pieces in a bunch of fractions.

$$\frac{2}{4}+\frac{3}{4}=\frac{5}{4}$$

And if you add another fourth, that's $6/4$. Add a few more to get $11/4$, then maybe take some away.

$$\frac{11}{4}-\frac{3}{4}=\frac{8}{4}$$, counting down this time.

You can keep going forever, as long as you are only talking about fourths.

➢ *The line in a fraction means "divided by"*

Think of the division symbol "÷" as a little picture of a fraction. The dots stand for the numerator and denominator.

In the late Middle Ages, European mathematicians took up the Arab habit of using a line to indicate division. Being lazy, they appreciated not having to write the whole division problem every time. When they wrote a fraction, they had the problem and its answer in one step.

$$7 \div 3 = \frac{7}{3}$$

Of course, they could change it into a mixed number, but why bother? Mathematicians don't mind using improper fractions, if that helps them solve a problem. (They do, however, insist the fraction be in lowest terms. See page 50.)

Your children will use this historical insight to put fractions on their calculators. When my son Jonathan needs to find a decimal equivalent for $\frac{7}{3}$, he simply types "7 ÷ 3" and reads the answer. Then in this case, he would have to round off, since thirds never end.

$$\frac{7}{3} = 7 \div 3 = 2.3333333\ldots \approx 2.3$$

This is also why the remainder in a division problem turns into a fraction. The fraction is like a miniature division problem. The four cookies that were left at the end of the last chapter, divided between 12 people, made

$$4 \div 12 = \frac{4}{12} = \frac{1}{3} \text{ (in lowest terms) cookie per person.}$$

Knowing that the line in a fraction means "divided by" will be important in algebra, when Jonathan meets alien monster fractions like $(64x^3 - 8)/(4x - 2)$. That is one reason we come back to this fact in junior high school:

A fraction is a division problem.

➢ Denominator: the fraction's family name

The bottom number of a fraction is its last name, or family name. All fractions with the same last name are in the same family.

The family name tells what size the pieces are—which is the same as saying how many of the pieces make one whole thing. With fourths, it takes four of them to make a whole. With sevenths, it takes seven of them.

This is why, as the last name gets bigger, the fraction itself gets smaller:

$$\frac{2}{7} < \frac{2}{4}$$

...because both have two pieces, but sevenths are smaller pieces than fourths.

Tolstoy said, "A man is like a fraction whose numerator is what he is and whose denominator is what he thinks of himself. The larger the denominator, the smaller the fraction."[18]

Pictures of fractions

There are three basic ways children can imagine a fraction. Teach all three to give your students a well-rounded understanding:

1. Circle fractions: Pizza slices

This is the easiest way for most of us to visualize fractions. We are used to cutting up pizza or pumpkin pie into various-sized slices, depending on the number of people we are serving. And because children like pizza, this makes fractions seem less threatening.

2. Rectangle fractions: A pan of brownies

Don't cut the rectangle diagonally, like a club sandwich. Use horizontal or vertical lines—more like cutting a sheet cake or a pan of brownies. Just as rectangles were a useful tool in understanding multiplication, cut-up rectangles help children learn fraction multiplication.

3. Parts of a group

This is the least natural way to understand fractions.

The denominator is how many are in the group, and the numerator is the number of parts you are talking about: "Three out of five dentists surveyed..." is the fraction $3/5$. If I have six apples, but two of them have gone bad, then $4/6$ of my apples are still edible.

Even though these fractions seem awkward, they are important in understanding later topics like percents and probability.

The fraction matching game

Have your child help you make ***Fraction Cards***:

- Take 3" x 5" index cards, and cut them in half. (Full-size would work, but smaller cards are easier to handle.)

- On each card, either write a fraction or draw its picture. Make sure that each "book" of fraction cards contains all three of the fraction pictures.

  That is, one card may say "½." It would match a picture of a circle with a line across the middle and one half colored in—and a rectangle with one half colored—and a group of two apples (small circles) with one colored. (Four cards total.)

  A card that said "2/2" would match a circle with a line across the middle and *both* halves colored in, a rectangle cut in half and *all* colored, and a group of two apples that are *both* colored.

- A good set of fraction cards to make: ½, 2/2; ⅓, ⅔, 3/3; ¼, 2/4, ¾, 4/4; 2/6, 3/6, 4/6, 6/6; 2/8, 4/8, 6/8, 8/8.

  You may also want to add fifths and tenths, but this makes a huge deck, which I find unwieldy. When children understand the simpler fractions, they can apply that knowledge to any fraction they meet.

- When you think the deck is finished, lay the cards out on the table in books, to make sure each card has all its mates. Every book should have one fraction card and three picture cards.

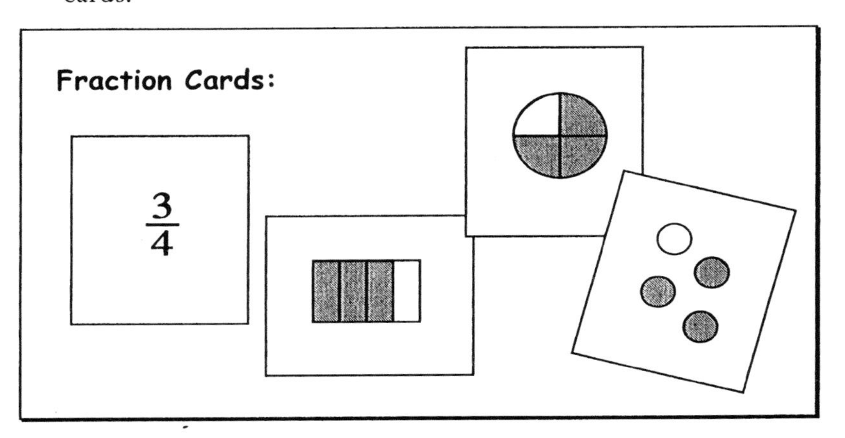

Use the fraction cards to play *Concentration*: Lay them all face down on the table, then try to turn up two matching cards—any two cards from a book of fractions. Or play *Go Fish*, according to your family's favorite rules. Both of these games help children become familiar and comfortable with fractions.

Working with fraction families

Here's the catch: **You can only add or subtract fractions that are in the same family.**

Fractions work something like fruit. You can't add apples and oranges, right? Well, you *can* add apples and oranges if you rename them first. Apples and oranges are both fruit. So two apples plus three oranges is five pieces of fruit.

In the same way, your children can add halves and fourths, or thirds and fifths, or any combination of fractions—if they first rename the fractions into the same family. (Math textbooks call this making *equivalent fractions* with a *common denominator.*)

Imagine leftover pizza for lunch. If there is ½ a pizza left and two hungry kids, Mom cuts the pizza. Now there are two pieces, but they are smaller—two fourths instead of one half. Mom just renamed the fraction into a new family.

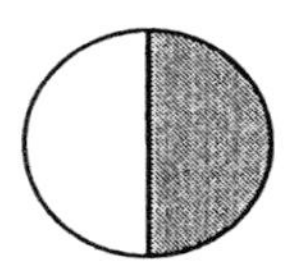

$$\frac{1}{2} = \frac{2}{4}$$

family = halves   family = fourths

If Mom wanted to eat, too, she might cut the half pizza into three pieces, which would give her:

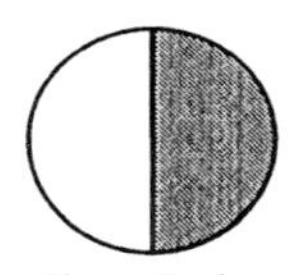

$$\frac{1}{2} = \frac{3}{6}$$

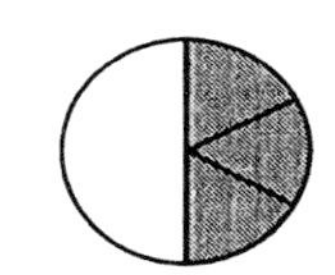

family = halves   family = sixths

Notice that when the number of pieces (numerator) doubled, the size of the pieces (denominator) *changed in the same proportion.* When the numerator tripled, so did the denominator.

But of course, the larger number in the denominator means *smaller* pieces of pizza.

Does it always work that way? Have your children experiment with construction paper pizzas, or simply draw circles on paper and divide them up.

⇒ **What if they cut ½ pizza into four pieces—what size would the pieces be?**

⇒ **What if they cut five pieces?**

Remember, the denominator, or family name, tells the size. That is, it tells how many pieces they would need to make one whole pizza.

See if your kids can find a rule that would always tell them what size the pieces will be, even if they *don't* start with a half.

⇒ **What if they cut ⅓ pizza into 100 pieces—what would they have then? (The correct answer is not "pizza crumbs"!)**

Equivalent fractions

When Mom sliced up the pizza to share it out for lunch, she changed her fraction from one family to another:

$$\frac{1}{2} = \frac{2}{4} = \frac{3}{6}$$

There were more pieces in each of Mom's new fractions, but the pieces were smaller. The total amount of pizza stayed the same. Two fractions that stand for the same total amount of stuff are called *equivalent fractions*.

> If you multiply both
> the top and bottom numbers of a fraction
> by the same number,
> the answer is an equivalent fraction.

This is a very easy pattern. Most children should have no problem understanding it, given plenty of hands-on experience. Practice slicing silly pizzas as an oral story problem:

⇒ **One fourth of a pizza will make how many 64ths?**

⇒ **Or one third is how many 390ths?**

Remember to take turns. Let your students challenge you to solve one. Half of the fun for children is trying to stump Mom.

Another game: Equivalent Fraction Rummy

Use your fraction cards to play ***Equivalent Fraction Rummy.***

Deal ten cards to each player and use the rules from Multiplication Rummy (page 27). This time, a player may meld any set of three (or more) equivalent fraction cards—*but the set must contain cards representing at least two different fractions.*

One valid meld would be the $\frac{1}{3}$ and $\frac{2}{6}$ cards, plus one or more of the pictures that go with them. Or a player might lay down the $\frac{4}{8}$ card with a picture of $\frac{1}{2}$ and another of $\frac{2}{4}$. Players may also lay down cards that match their own existing melds, but they can't build on another player's set.

Lowest terms

When you are sure your children understand how to make equivalent fractions, add a new twist. Point out that equivalent fractions work backwards, too. (They may have noticed this already.)

Division is backwards multiplication. Your children can *divide* both the top and bottom of their original fraction by the same number. This makes a new equivalent fraction. It is as if Mom stuck her pizza together to change from $\frac{3}{6}$ back to the original $\frac{1}{2}$.

This is how you get the fraction into *lowest terms.* Lowest terms means having the smallest denominator—the largest pieces—you can get. If your kids are like mine, they will understand the importance of large pieces when it comes to pizza.

> The fraction in lowest terms
> is always the easiest form of the fraction
> to understand.

Ask you children to imagine $\frac{12}{16}$. Can they make a mental picture of that? Could they measure out $\frac{12}{16}$ of a cup of flour? How about $\frac{3}{4}$—that's simpler, right?

Whenever your children work fraction problems, have them give the answers in lowest terms. This is not busywork. It is good manners.

The dreaded common denominator

Remember: **You can only add or subtract fractions that are in the same family.**

But what if my son Jonathan has to add $\frac{2}{3} + \frac{1}{5}$?

That "same family" that lets you add two fractions is called the *common* (or shared) *denominator* of those two fractions. Once a student understands how to make equivalent fractions, he should have little problem getting two fractions into the same family.

An easy way to find common denominators is by using a *smallest common multiple chart.* Give your child a piece of graph paper with a large grid. Have him write the numbers one to twelve across the top of the paper and down the left side. Where each row and column meet, tell him to fill in the smallest common multiple of those numbers—the smallest number they both will divide evenly into.

1	2	3	4	5	...
2	2	6	4	10	...
3	6	3	12	15	...
4	4	12	4	20	...
5	10	15	20	5	...
6	6	6	12	30	...

Jonathan's problem was $\frac{2}{3} + \frac{1}{5}$. When making equivalent fractions, he can use any multiple of the two denominators to make a common family name. He could turn $\frac{2}{3} + \frac{1}{5}$ into $\frac{110}{165} + \frac{33}{165}$, but he would be crazy to do so.

To make things easy, he should pick the smallest number he can turn thirds and fifths into. That is why they call it the ***least common denominator***. "Least common" doesn't mean the rarest, it means the smallest one they share.

Jonathan can use his chart to find the smallest multiple that three and five share, which is fifteen, then use the equivalent fractions rule to rename the fractions. If he wants to change $\frac{2}{3}$ into fifteenths, he will multiply the top and bottom numbers of his fraction by 5. To change ⅕ into fifteenths, he needs to multiply by 3.

$$\frac{2}{3}=\frac{2\times 5}{3\times 5}=\frac{10}{15} \quad \text{and} \quad \frac{1}{5}=\frac{1\times 3}{5\times 3}=\frac{3}{15}$$

So...

$$\frac{2}{3}+\frac{1}{5}=\frac{10}{15}+\frac{3}{15}=\frac{13}{15}$$

When he gets the fractions into the same family, all he has to do is count up the number of pieces. Ten pieces and three more pieces make a total of 13 pieces. That's not so hard after all.

Subtraction works the same way: First, get both of the fractions into the same family by finding a common denominator. Then you can subtract.

Fractions can be easy, when you keep it all in the family!

A puzzle for advanced students:

The epitaph of Diophantus

This tomb holds Diophantus. Ah, what a marvel!

And the tomb tells scientifically the measure of his life. God vouchsafed that he should be a boy for the sixth part of his life; when a twelfth was added, his cheeks acquired a beard; He kindled for him the light of marriage after a seventh, and in the fifth year after his marriage He granted him a son.

Alas! late-begotten and miserable child, when he had reached the measure of half his father's life, the chill grave took him.

After consoling his grief by this science of numbers for four years, he reached the end of his life.[19]

Mathematics has the dubious honor of being the least popular subject in the curriculum. Future teachers pass through the elementary schools learning to detest mathematics. They return to the elementary schools to teach a new generation to detest it.

—*Time magazine*[20]

More Fractions: Sharing a Pan of Brownies

If children can count, they can add and subtract fractions—match the fraction family, then count up to add or down to subtract. But most people have no idea what is really happening when they multiply or divide with fractions.

Could you explain the fraction rules on page 41? If not, don't make your children memorize them.

Without understanding, rules get tangled in a child's mind. If the shortcut works for multiplying, he reasons, it should make adding easier, too. Why bother to find a common denominator, when he can just add the top and bottom?

$$\frac{2}{3}+\frac{1}{5}=\frac{3}{8} \text{ Right? No!}$$

But *why* is it wrong?

It is wrong because the student hasn't applied his common sense. Multiplication is not the same as addition. Addition is like counting more or fewer pieces of pizza. But multiplication is like cutting the pizza into different-sized pieces. It should not be a surprise that the rules are different.

"Of" means multiply

Instead of merely teaching the rules, take your children back to the three pictures of multiplication: groups, jumps, and rectangles. What does it mean to multiply two numbers?

Imagine four Easter baskets *of* six eggs each—how many eggs? Or two jumps *of* seven spaces on the number line—how far? Or a rectangle with five rows *of* five blocks, for 5 x 5 = 25 blocks in all.

Now imagine half *of* an egg basket, or one seventh *of* a jump, or three fifths *of* that rectangle.

If you want to understand fractions, here is the most important hint in this book:

The multiplication symbol means "of."

When children can translate a multiplication problem, they easily see how to work it.

$\frac{1}{2} \times 16$ = "one half of 16"

This is a valuable key to solving fraction and percent problems. I say it so often that my son Jonathan has started to roll his eyes at me. *"Of means multiply. Multiply means of. I've got it already!"* But I want him to know it in his bones, so I keep repeating it.

- $\frac{1}{3} \times 12 = \frac{1}{3}$ of $12 = 4$
- $\frac{7}{10} \times 100 = \frac{7}{10}$ of $100 = 70$
- $\frac{5}{4} \times 36 = \frac{5}{4}$ of $36 = 45$
  First find $\frac{1}{4}$, then count up 5 of them.
- "Of" always means multiply!

For a story problem example: When I was a kid we had a gray tomcat named Jingle, who slept $\frac{2}{3}$ of every day. How many hours was he on the prowl? I could figure his sleep time and subtract that from 24 hours, but it is simpler to go straight to the third of the day that he was awake:

One third *of* each day = $\frac{1}{3} \times 24$ hours = 8 hours of activity.

The second hint

I have already told you the second step in understanding fraction multiplication. It is so simple, you may not have noticed it fly by. You will want to point it out to your children, however, so pay attention this time.

"...First find ¼, then count up 5 of them."

Or, in more general terms...

First, find what *one* of the fractional pieces would be. Then multiply by how many of them you have.

Mathematicians are lazy. They always do the easy part first. For most of us, it is easy to visualize one third or one half or one twelfth of a thing.

After your child has figured out that ¼ of 36 equals 9, it is a snap for him to see that five of those fourths make:

$$5 \times \left(\frac{1}{4} \textit{ of } 36\right) = 5 \times 9 = 45$$

Your child can use this two-step process to understand almost every fraction multiplication problem he meets.

1. "Of" means multiply, so what is the fraction *of*?

What is ¼ x ¹⁄₁₂? This means find ¼ of ¹⁄₁₂. Imagine a pizza cut into twelve pieces, then one of those twelfths cut into four pieces. What size is one of those slivers compared to the whole pizza? Well, if I cut all of the twelfths into four pieces, there would be 48 tiny pieces in the whole pizza. So ¼ of ¹⁄₁₂ is one forty-eighth.

$$\frac{1}{4} \times \frac{1}{12} = \frac{1}{48}$$

2. Before trying to figure out the whole answer, what is *one* piece of the fraction equal to?

What is ¾ x ⅔? First, find ¼ of ⅔. Imagine cutting a pan of brownies into thirds and serving out ⅓ for snacks. You would have ⅔ of the pan left—what is one fourth of this? Since there are already two pieces (thirds), if you cut each piece in half you would have four pieces. One fourth of ⅔ is the same as half of a third, or ⅙. And three of those fourths will be 3/6, which put in lowest terms is ½.

$$\frac{3}{4} \times \frac{2}{3} = \frac{1}{2}$$

Cutting up the brownies

When your child is trying to imagine multiplying fractions, he can use whichever of the multiplication pictures (page 26) best helps him understand. Have him think of splitting a group into thirds, taking only one-fourth of a skip on the number line, or cutting one whole rectangle into fractional pieces.

In the second example above, I used the rectangle—or pan of brownies—model to visualize the multiplication. Rainbow Resource sells ***Frac-Multi*** and ***Frac-Divide***, two inexpensive sets of transparent cards that use this model to show hundreds of fraction combinations. You may want to spend several days playing mix-and-match games.

> **This is how the rectangle model of fractions works: The number one stands for one whole pan of brownies, and the fractions are pieces of the whole.**

Say there was half a pan of brownies left after my husband and kids tromped through the kitchen and snarfed some. If I put half of *that* on a plate to share at the ladies' Bible study, then my pan is down to ½ of ½, which is ¼ of the original pan.

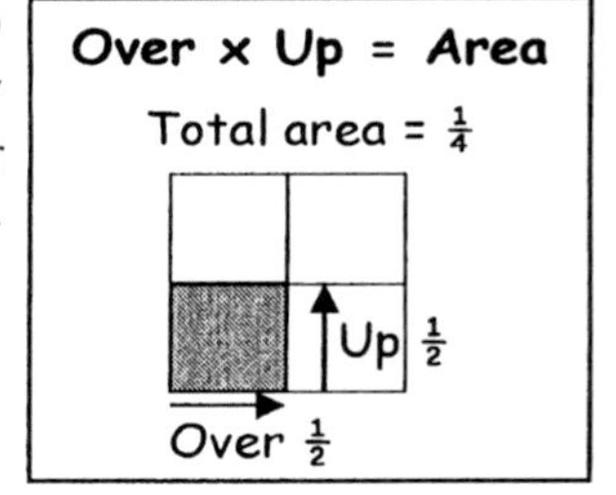

Use the basic rectangle relationship that your children used to multiply and divide with base ten blocks. Over times up is area, so how big is a rectangle ½ over by ½ up?

It is ¼ of a 1 x 1 square:

$$\frac{1}{2} \times \frac{1}{2} = \frac{1}{4}$$

Let's try another example: How could my son Jonathan figure out the fraction problem ⅗ x ¼?

He starts by drawing a large rectangle to stand for the pan of brownies. Since *over* times *up* is *area*, he needs to draw a section of brownie that is ⅗ over by ¼ up.

The total area of that section will be his answer.

He draws vertical lines to split the over dimension into fifths. Then he draws horizontal lines to split the up dimension fourths. That divides the pan of brownies into 20 small pieces.

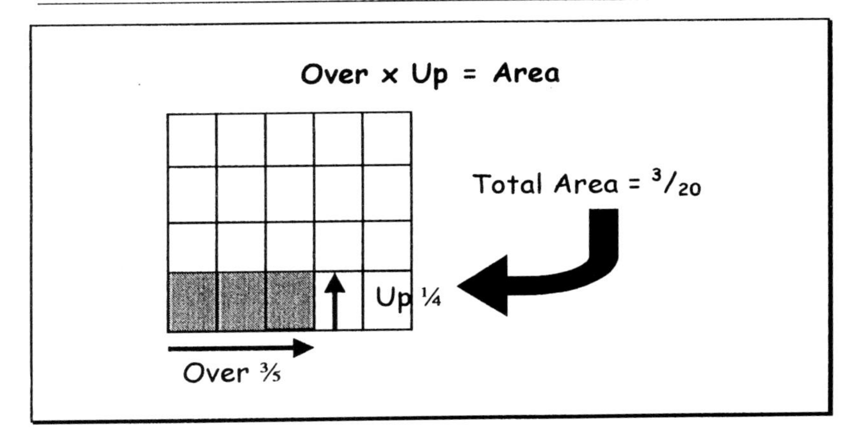

To find his answer, Jonathan colors the part of the rectangle that is *over three* of the fifths and *up one* of the fourths. This turns out to be three of the 20 small squares that make up the whole rectangle.

$$\frac{3}{5} \times \frac{1}{4} = \frac{3}{20}$$

Look for the pattern

There is a pattern that makes multiplying fractions super-easy. But please, don't tell your students the rule at first. Instead, have them work through several multiplication problems with pans of brownies. See if they spot it on their own.

After a few days of drawing multiplication problems, if they don't seem to notice the pattern, tell them it exists—"You know, there's a trick that makes this simple..."—but don't give it away. Ask them to look back over their work and try to identify the pattern. Here is the rule you want them to find:

> **To multiply two fractions,**
> **you multiply the numerators**
> **and multiply the denominators.**

To say it in symbols, where the letters stand for whatever numbers are in the fractions you want to multiply:

$$\frac{a}{b} \times \frac{c}{d} = \frac{a \times c}{b \times d}$$

If your students figure the pattern out, see if they can explain why it works. Discovering the pattern for themselves will help to fix it in their minds. But when they figure out how to explain it, you will know they understand.

Here is why the rule works: When you draw the pan of brownies for a fraction multiplication problem, there are always two rectangles in your sketch.

1. The smaller rectangle is the number of pieces in your answer fraction—the numerator. It is always the product of the numerators of the two fractions you are multiplying.
2. The larger rectangle is the pan itself. It tells you the size of the pieces in your answer fraction—the denominator, which is the number of pieces there would be if you had one whole pan of brownies. And this is always the product of the denominators of the two fractions you are multiplying.

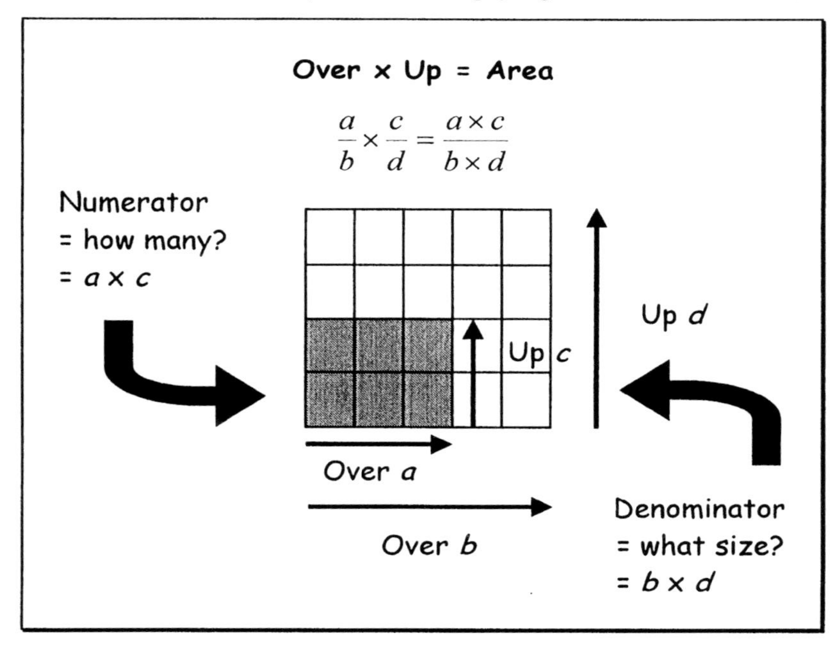

When your students understand this pattern and know why it works, they will discover that multiplying fractions is even easier than adding them. No need to mess with a common denominator, just multiply the top and multiply the bottom—and remember to put the answer in lowest terms!

A double batch of brownies

Children get confused when they have to work with fractions greater than one. We all think of a fraction as something small, so we find mixed numbers and improper fractions harder to visualize. Nevertheless, the rectangle relationships are true no matter what size rectangle your child has to solve.

This time, we will try a division problem:

Area divided by ***up*** equals ***over***. So what is $7/4 \div 1/2$?

First, we need to get the total area: $7/4$, which is one pan of brownies plus $3/4$ of a second pan. Then we need to arrange this amount of stuff into a rectangle that is $1/2$ up. When we find out how far over this rectangle goes, that will tell us how many $1/2$'s there are in $7/4$—that is, the over dimension gives our answer.

Don't try to do this in your head. Start by drawing the area—a double batch of brownies, with the second pan taste-tested in one corner. Area = $7/4$. Now, draw a new picture to show the pieces rearranged to make a rectangle that is $1/2$ up. How far over will they go?

The over dimension is the answer to our division problem:

$$7/4 \div 1/2 = 3\frac{1}{2}$$

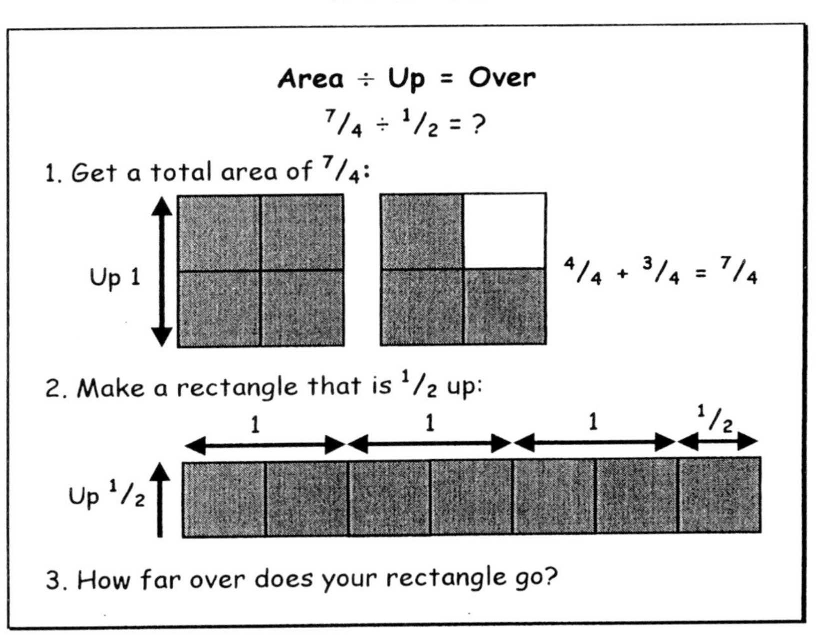

Division is backwards multiplication

The pan of brownies model gives students a way to visualize fraction division, but it gets to be a cumbersome nuisance. You won't want to use it with any but the simplest problems.

If your student truly understands how to multiply fractions, he should be able to handle fraction division. Remember, division is like multiplication done backwards.

Consider again the problem $7/4 \div 1/2 = ?$

Because division is backwards multiplication, we can turn the problem around. *What* times ½ will make 7/4?

$$\frac{7}{4} \div \frac{1}{2} \Rightarrow \frac{[?]}{[?]} \times \frac{1}{2} = \frac{7}{4}$$

Sometimes, turning a division problem around makes the answer obvious. If you know how to multiply fractions, you can see at a glance what needs to go in the brackets.

$$\frac{7}{2} \times \frac{1}{2} = \frac{7}{4} \text{ so } \frac{7}{4} \div \frac{1}{2} = \frac{7}{2}$$

...and if you want a mixed number, you can change the answer to 3½.

Can you always use "division is backwards multiplication" to solve fraction division problems? Yes, it always works. And it's a wonderful trick, because every time your student uses it, he is reinforcing his understanding of what division really means.

Not every problem can be solved at a glance, of course. Most will take more than one step. Here is a slightly harder example:

$$\frac{1}{3} \div \frac{1}{4} = ?$$

This transforms into the multiplication problem:

$$\frac{[?]}{[?]} \times \frac{1}{4} = \frac{1}{3}$$

Your student may protest: "You can't multiply fourths to get thirds!"

At first thought, this does seem impossible. If your child is stuck on this, it's time for some Socratic questioning...

- What do you know about the answers in fraction problems?

- Does Mom ever give you back your homework and tell you to change an answer, even though you worked the problem right? Why would a teacher do that?
- What do you always have to do to the answer in a fraction problem?

It may take some coaxing, asking the question in several different ways, but eventually your student should come up with, "I have to put the answer in lowest terms."

In the multiplication problem:

$$\frac{[?]}{[?]} \times \frac{1}{4} = \frac{1}{3}$$

...what is the answer? Not the number that we are trying to find—what is the answer to the multiplication problem itself?

It is the product, $\frac{1}{3}$.

Now, have your student consider: Could that "$\frac{1}{3}$" actually be some equivalent fraction that has been put into lowest terms? In particular, could it be a fraction with a denominator that is a multiple of four, perhaps 3×4 = twelfths?

$$\frac{1}{3} = \frac{1 \times 4}{3 \times 4} = \frac{4}{12}$$

That would make the multiplication problem look like this:

$$\frac{[?]}{[?]} \times \frac{1}{4} = \frac{4}{12}$$

Aha! That's easy:

$$\frac{4}{3} \times \frac{1}{4} = \frac{4}{12}$$

...which gives us the answer to our division problem:

$$\frac{1}{3} \div \frac{1}{4} = \frac{4}{3}$$

Let's try one more example, still harder. What is $\frac{7}{5} \div \frac{2}{3}$?

Begin by turning the division around to make this multiplication problem:

$$\frac{[?]}{[?]} \times \frac{2}{3} = \frac{7}{5}$$

Again, the $\frac{7}{5}$ must be some equivalent fraction in lowest terms. But what could it be? Well, the numerator of the equivalent fraction had to be something times two. Perhaps it was:

$$\frac{7}{5}=\frac{7\times 2}{5\times 2}=\frac{14}{10}$$

Remember, when making an equivalent fraction, you have to multiply the top (numerator) and the bottom (denominator) by the same number.

So, now our multiplication problem looks like this:

$$\frac{[?]}{[?]}\times\frac{2}{3}=\frac{14}{10}$$

That's closer, but the denominator of the equivalent fraction must have been something times three:

$$\frac{14}{10}=\frac{14\times 3}{10\times 3}=\frac{42}{30}$$

$$\frac{[?]}{[?]}\times\frac{2}{3}=\frac{42}{30}$$

Aha! Now we can solve it.

$$\frac{21}{10}\times\frac{2}{3}=\frac{42}{30}$$

...and going back to our original division problem:

$$\frac{7}{5}\div\frac{2}{3}=\frac{21}{10}$$

If division with fractions is too difficult for your elementary student to grasp, drop it. Give him a few years, and come back to it in junior high. As a young person's thinking skills develop, he will find abstraction much easier to handle.

"Ours is not to reason why, just invert and multiply!"

What about the division rule, "Flip it over and multiply"? Yes, by all means teach your children that—*if* you can make them understand *why*.

The trick "division is backwards multiplication" is based on your child's understanding of what the fraction problem really means. But "flip it over and multiply" is just a recipe learned by rote. If your child does not understand why the rule works, he may still be able to pass a chapter test. But he will forget the rule as soon as you stop drilling him on it.

He won't completely forget, however. In the back of his mind will remain a nagging suspicion that he should flip a fraction over when he wants to multiply. Unfortunately, that garbled memory will ruin any hope he has of understanding fractions at all.

(In case you are in any doubt: You ***should not*** flip a fraction over when you want to multiply!)

What humans do
with the language of mathematics
is to describe patterns.

To grow mathematically,
children must be exposed to a rich variety
of patterns appropriate to their own lives
through which they can see
variety, regularity,
and interconnections.

—Lynn Arthur Steen[21]

***

Looking for patterns trains the mind
to search out and discover the similarities
that bind seemingly unrelated information
together in a whole.

A child who expects things to "make sense"
looks for the sense in things
and from this develops understanding.

A child who does not see patterns
often does not *expect* things to make sense
and sees all events as discrete,
separate,
and unrelated.

—Mary Baratta-Lorton[22]

There are two aims which the teacher must have in view: First, to help the student to solve the problem at hand. Second, to develop the student's ability so that he may solve future problems by himself.

—*George Polyá*[23]

Fractions in Disguise

By the time they reach junior high school, most students are ready for abstract reasoning. Now is the time to dig into the math topics that give younger children stomach cramps—especially if you can keep the attitude that math is a game of discovery.

What is a fraction, again?

Your junior high or high school student needs to know three things about fractions:

- A fraction is a division problem.
- A fraction is a comparison.
- A fraction is a reciprocal.

These ways of understanding a fraction are all true for every fraction in every situation. They are inherent in the definition of *fraction.* They are simply different ways of looking at the same fraction.

If your child can understand one of them, he will understand fractions a little. If he can understand them all, he will have mastered fractions—and he will be able to choose which way of looking at the fraction will be most useful for solving any given problem.

For practice solving fraction, decimal, ratio, and percent problems, get the book **When Are We Ever Gonna Have To**

Use *This?* by Hal Saunders. Your children can figure the cost of newspaper ads, determine a patient's proper dose of medication, or decide how to balance the load in an airplane to keep the center of gravity within safe limits.

I know of no better way to build understanding than with real-life problems.

A fraction is a division problem: Decimals

Go back and review how to read a fraction: The line in a fraction means *divided by*. Make up and solve a few monster division problems like 624 ÷ 156 by writing them as fractions and converting to lowest terms.

$$624 \div 156 = \frac{624}{156} = \frac{312}{78} = \frac{156}{39} = \frac{52}{13} = 4$$

Now try these:

$$270 \div 45 = \frac{270}{45} = ?$$

$$1344 \div 168 = \frac{1344}{168} = ?$$

$$1584 \div 792 = \frac{1584}{792} = ?$$

Use this fact about fractions to convert any standard fraction into a decimal fraction (a number written with a decimal point). A calculator is handy for this. Simply enter the division problem, numerator ÷ denominator, and read off the answer to as many decimal places as you wish.

Practice changing fractions to decimals, like these examples:

$$\frac{3}{4} = 3 \div 4 = 0.75$$

$$\frac{35}{10} = 35 \div 10 = 3.5$$

$$\frac{8}{27} = 0.296...$$

Can your child figure out how to go the other way, converting a decimal to a fraction?

> For decimal fractions,
> the denominators are multiples of ten:
> tenths, hundredths, thousandths, etc.
>
> 1/8 = 1 ÷ 8 = 0.125 = 125/1000 = 1/8
>
> Be careful when counting decimal place value.
> There are never any one-ths, because 8/1 = just plain 8.

As they work with decimals, teach your children to estimate how big the answer should be. For instance, consider:

$$0.2 \times 0.3 = ?$$

The decimal 0.2 is $\frac{2}{10}$, which is the same as $\frac{1}{5}$. And 0.3 is about $\frac{1}{3}$. If you remember that the multiplication symbol means "of," you know the answer is about $\frac{1}{5}$ of $\frac{1}{3}$—that's small!

If your child answers 0.2 x 0.3 = 0.6, he needs to try again.

This is especially important when using a calculator, because hitting the wrong button can make big errors. For instance, 20.75 x 18.3 rounds off to 20 x 20, so the answer had better be close to 400. If your child's calculator gives him 37.9, he entered the problem wrong.

A good, hands-on way to teach decimals is with money. Let children earn it, spend it, figure sales tax—even loan it to you and collect interest. Money is a powerfully motivating manipulative.

A fraction is a division problem: Canceling out

NOTE: Canceling out only works on **multiplication** *problems! Do not let your child try to cancel out numbers in addition or subtraction.*

Because the line in a fraction means "divided by":

$$\frac{2}{2} = 2 \div 2 = 1 \quad \text{and} \quad \frac{3}{3} = 3 \div 3 = 1 \quad \text{and} \quad \frac{35}{35} = 35 \div 35 = 1$$

...and so forth.

Any time there is the same number in the numerator and denominator of a fraction, those two numbers *cancel out*—that is, they divide out to make one.

To put a fraction into lowest terms, your child can try canceling out. He finds a factor that is in both the numerator and denominator, then he divides that factor by itself to make one.

Since one times any number is simply that number itself, your child can cross out the canceled factors and ignore them.

$$\frac{9}{12} = \frac{\cancel{3} \times 3}{\cancel{3} \times 4} = \frac{3}{4} \quad \text{(The 3's cancel, because } 3 \div 3 = 1.)$$

$$\frac{30}{36} = \frac{5 \times \cancel{6}}{\cancel{6} \times 6} = \frac{5}{6} \quad \text{(The 6's cancel, because } 6 \div 6 = 1.)$$

Your child can often save a step by doing the factoring in his head. That is, he can recognize that both 9 and 12 have a factor of three, without writing out the factors. He would cross out the 9 and write the remaining 3 beside it, and he would cross out the 12 and write the remaining 4 beside it:

$$\frac{\cancel{9}(3)}{\cancel{12}(4)} = \frac{3}{4}$$

The big advantage of canceling out is that your student can often do it *before* he multiplies. In the following example, both the 6's and the 4's canceled out. This makes the answer come out in lowest terms automatically.

$$\frac{3}{(5)\cancel{30}} \times \frac{\cancel{6}}{\cancel{4}} \times \frac{\cancel{4}}{7} = \frac{3}{35}$$

Watch out for a common mistake

When your child is canceling out, he is making ones.

$$\frac{4}{4} = 4 \div 4 = 1 \text{, etc.}$$

Since any number times one is itself, he can usually ignore the one.

But if *all* the numbers in the numerator or denominator of his fraction cancel out, he needs to remember that one, because it is still there. He can never cancel everything and get zero.

A fraction is a comparison: Ratios & percents

Equivalent fractions are like those vocabulary ratios on the SAT: "Gargantuan is to colossal as miniscule is to ___(*diminutive*)___." In the same way...

$$\frac{1}{2}=\frac{3}{6}$$

...means, "One is to two as three is to six."[24]

This may seem like a trick or gimmick, but the idea of ratios is basic to understanding percent problems. Ratios are also useful in solving for algebraic unknowns.

Algebra first, because it is easy

Make up a few problems, and have your children figure out how they could make the equivalent fractions. What numbers would make the equations true?

$$\frac{1}{2}=\frac{x}{16}$$

Your children can picture easy ratios like "1 is to 2 as x is to 16" in their heads. For harder ones, use the balance rule:

> You can do anything you want to an equation,
> as long as you keep the equation balanced
> by doing the same thing to both sides.

To solve the ratio "n is to 12 as 13 is to 52," I have to isolate the n.

$$\frac{n}{12}=\frac{13}{52}$$

I want to end up with n = some number. I can take advantage of "canceling out" to solve my problem. If I multiply both sides by 12, the 12's on the left-hand side of the equation will cancel, leaving n by itself.

$$\frac{n}{\cancel{12}}\times \cancel{12}=\frac{13}{52}\times 12$$

$$n=3$$

Percents are ratios, too

> Percents always have a denominator of 100,
> so 75% = 75/100.
> The percent sign means *per hundred.*
>
> Since 100% is one whole thing,
> the denominator of your ratio will be
> whatever number stands for one whole thing.

If your student needs 75% to pass a physics test, and there are 36 questions overall, then the comparison is:

$$\frac{75}{100} = \frac{q}{36}$$

75 is to 100 as *what* is to 36?

Use the balance rule to solve this, multiplying both sides of the equation by 36, which gives $q = 27$. He must get at least 27 questions right to pass.

Turn the comparison around: If your son missed four questions, for a score of 32 out of 36, what percent did he get right? This time the ratio is:

$$\frac{s}{100} = \frac{32}{36}$$

What is to 100 as 32 is to 36?

Again, use the balance rule, multiplying by 100. He scored about 89%.

Percents are meaningless by themselves

Percents are always a percent *of* something.

Remember that "of" means multiply. This gives your student another way to understand percent problems. They can write out the question that they want to answer, in ordinary English, and then translate it into an equation.

In our first example above, the question we wanted to answer was, "What is 75% of 36 questions?" *What* means the variable, the number we want to find. *Is* means an equal sign. 75% is the fraction 75/100. And of course, *of* means multiply.

In translation, our question looks like this:

$$q = \frac{75}{100} \times 36$$

In the second example above, the question was, "32 questions is what percent of 36?" Again, *what* is the unknown variable, *is* means equal, *of* means multiply, and the percent is a fraction with 100 as the denominator.

Translated into an equation, it becomes:

$$32 = \frac{s}{100} \times 36$$

This translation method will work for any percent problem. After your student figures out what the percent is *of*, he can put it into a question. Then he has practically solved the problem—the rest is calculator fodder.

A fraction is a comparison: Trigonometry

Trigonometry is the mathematics of relationships. In trigonometry, your students will study the ratios between the lengths of a triangle's sides, and they will study how those ratios relate to the angles.

In any triangle, the angles and the sides are related. The longest side is always opposite the widest angle, and the shortest side opposite the smallest angle. If you can measure one side and two angles, you can find out everything there is to know about the triangle.

In trigonometry, we usually use right triangles, so we know one of the angles automatically. That means we only need to measure two things—one side and an angle, or two of the sides—in order to find the height of a mountain, the width of a river, or the depth of a shipwreck on the ocean floor.

To see the trigonometric ratios, draw any right triangle. Mark the right angle with a little box, to show the lines are perpendicular. Now pick either of the other angles and call it *theta.*

(*Theta* is a Greek word, pronounced "Thay-tuh." It's the name of the Greek letter θ, which mathematicians use to name angles the same way they use x to name variables.)

It does not matter at all which angle you choose. In real life, surveyors and engineers pick whichever angle is easiest to measure.

Next, look at the sides of your triangle. The side opposite the right angle is always called the *hypotenuse*. The other sides are called *legs*. Label the leg close to your angle *adjacent* and the farther one *opposite*. The trig ratios compare the lengths of these sides. The sine, abbreviated *sin*, compares the opposite side to the hypotenuse. The cosine, abbreviated *cos*, compares the adjacent side to the hypotenuse. And the tangent, *tan* for short, compares the two legs.

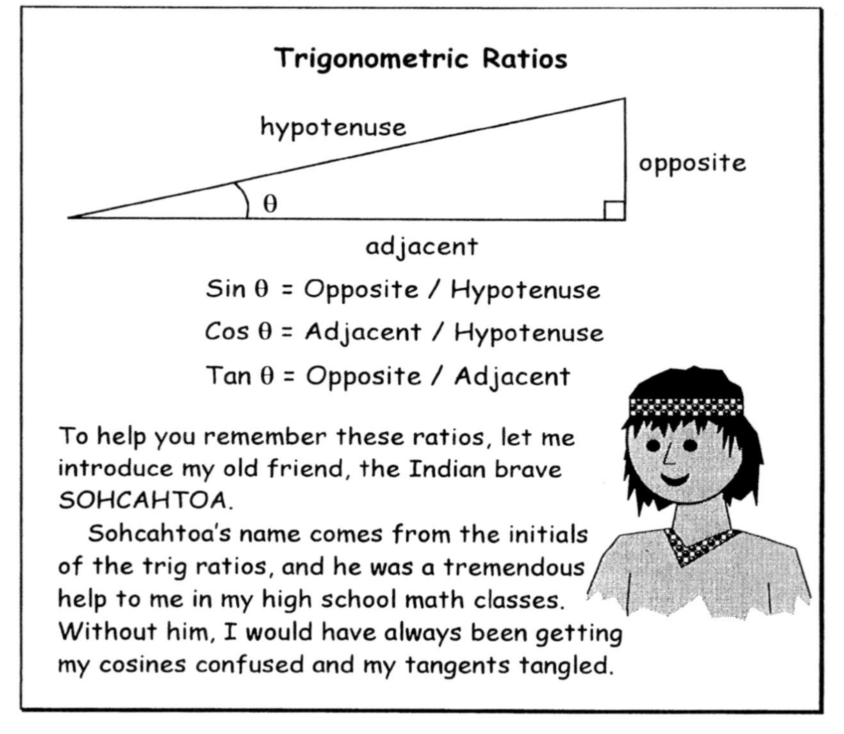

I don't have room to explain how these ratios are used to solve problems. The main point I want to make here is this:

These trig ratios are merely fractions in disguise.

If your student understands fractions, he can apply that knowledge to working with trigonometry. It will make his high school life much easier.

A fraction is a reciprocal: Conversion factors

A fraction is a reciprocal, *a number that has been flipped over.*

- The reciprocal of 5 is $\frac{1}{5}$.
- The reciprocal of $\frac{2}{3}$ is $\frac{3}{2}$.
- The reciprocal of x is $\frac{1}{x}$.

Reciprocals work backwards, too. The reciprocal of $\frac{1}{2}$ is $\frac{2}{1}$, which is 2, and the reciprocal of $\frac{1}{x}$ is x.[25]

You child will use reciprocals mostly for *conversion factors*—special fractions that contain problem-solving information:

⇒ *Conversion* means change, because conversion factors help you change the numbers in your problem.

⇒ *Factors* are things you multiply with. So to use a conversion factor, your child will multiply it by something.

For instance, if I am driving an average of 60 mph on the highway, I can use that rate as a conversion factor.

I may use the fraction $\frac{60\text{ miles}}{1\text{ hour}}$,

...or I may flip it over to make $\frac{1\text{ hour}}{60\text{ miles}}$.

It all depends on what problem I want to solve. After driving two hours, I traveled:

$$2\text{ hours} \times \frac{60\text{ miles}}{1\text{ hour}} = 120\text{ miles so far.}$$

But if I am planning to go 240 more miles, and I need to know when I will arrive:

$$240\text{ miles} \times \frac{1\text{ hour}}{60\text{ miles}} = 4\text{ hours to go.}$$

Using conversion factors is like multiplying by one

If I am driving 60 mph, then driving for one hour is *the same as* driving for 60 miles, and...

$$\frac{60\text{ miles}}{1\text{ hour}} = 60\text{ miles} \div 1\text{ hour} = 1$$

This may be easier to see if you think of kitchen measurements. Two cups are *the same as* one pint, so:

$$\frac{2\,\text{cups}}{1\,\text{pint}} = 2\,\text{cups} \div 1\,\text{pint} = 1$$

If I want to find out how many cups are in 3 pints of flour, I can multiply by the conversion factor.

$$3\,\text{pints} \times \frac{2\,\text{cups}}{\text{pint}} = 6\,\text{cups}$$

Multiplying by one does not change the original number. In the same way, multiplying by a conversion factor does not change the original amount of stuff—only the units that you measure the stuff in. When I multiplied 3 pints times the conversion factor, I did not change the total amount of flour, only the way I measured it.

Conversion factors can always be flipped over

If there are 60 minutes/hour, there must be 1 hour/60 minutes.

$$\frac{60\,\text{minutes}}{1\,\text{hour}} \Leftrightarrow \frac{1\,\text{hour}}{60\,\text{minutes}}$$

If I draw up house plans at a scale of 4 feet/inch, that is the same as saying 1 inch/4 feet.

$$\frac{4\,\text{feet}}{1\,\text{inch}} \Leftrightarrow \frac{1\,\text{inch}}{4\,\text{feet}}$$

If there are 2 cups/pint, there is ½ pint/cup. Or if an airplane is burning fuel at 8 gallons/hour, the pilot has only ⅛ hour to fly for every gallon left in his tank.

This is true for all conversion factors, and it's part of what makes them so useful in solving problems. Your student can choose whichever form of the conversion factor seems most helpful in the problem at hand.

You can string conversion factors together

String several conversion factors together to solve more complicated problems. Just as numbers cancel out when they are on the top and bottom of a fraction (2/2 = 2 ÷ 2 = 1), units cancel if you have the same unit in the numerator and denominator. In the following example, gallons/gallons = gallons ÷ gallons = 1.

How many cups of milk are there in a gallon jug?

$$1\,\cancel{\text{gallon}} \times \frac{4\,\cancel{\text{quarts}}}{1\,\cancel{\text{gallon}}} \times \frac{2\,\cancel{\text{pints}}}{1\,\cancel{\text{quart}}} \times \frac{2\,\text{cups}}{1\,\cancel{\text{pint}}} = 16\,\text{cups}$$

Notice that only the units cancel out—not the number. Even after I cancelled out the "quarts," the "4" was still part of the equation.

Let's try one more. The true power of conversion factors is their ability to change one piece of information into something that at first glance seems to be unrelated to the number with which you started.

Suppose I drove for 45 minutes at 55 mph in a pickup truck that gets 18 miles to the gallon, and I want to know how much gas I used. To find out, I start with a number I know (45 minutes) and use conversion factors until I get the units I want for the answer (gallons of gas):

$$45\,\cancel{\text{min}}. \times \frac{1\,\cancel{\text{hour}}}{60\,\cancel{\text{min}}.} \times \frac{55\,\cancel{\text{miles}}}{\cancel{\text{hour}}} \times \frac{1\,\text{gallon}}{18\,\cancel{\text{miles}}} = 2.3\,\text{gallons}$$

Encourage your children to play around with conversion factors. They will be surprised how many problems these mathematical wonders can solve.

A fraction is a reciprocal: Flip it over and multiply

WARNING: This section is rated 100 on the abstraction meter scale and may cause extreme mental numbification. Proceed with caution.

A funny thing about reciprocals is that when you multiply them together, the answer is one.

$$2 \times \frac{1}{2} = 1$$

$$\frac{1}{5} \times 5 = 1$$

$$x \times \frac{1}{x} = 1$$

It always works that way. This fact is actually the definition of *reciprocal*, since "a flipped-over number" is not a mathematically precise term.

This leads to another strange property of reciprocals. To multiply something by any number is the same as dividing by that number's reciprocal.

$$16 \times \frac{1}{2} = 16 \div 2 = 8$$

$$25 \times \frac{1}{5} = 25 \div 5 = 5$$

It always works that way. It is inherent in the definition of reciprocal.

And to divide something by any number is the same as multiplying by that number's reciprocal.

$$16 \div 2 = 16 \times \frac{1}{2}$$

$$25 \div 5 = 25 \times \frac{1}{5}$$

$$x \div \frac{a}{b} = x \times \frac{b}{a}$$

It always works that way. It is inherent in the definition of reciprocal.

To divide by a fraction, you flip it over and multiply.

So now you understand why that rule never made sense when you learned it back in fifth grade.

Most students will not care about reciprocals. That's okay. Let them memorize the rule for dividing by a fraction and practice it without truly understanding. They should be old enough to handle that, now that they are in junior high, especially if they understood *most* of the stuff they have done with fractions. They will get by well enough.

But for the students who do enjoy abstraction, give them the challenge of *proving* that the rule is true. They will remember it better because they understand it.

And for kids who like abstraction, proofs are fun!

Only by wrestling with the conditions of the problem at first hand, seeking and finding his own way out, does he think.

—*John Dewey*[26]

Mathematical Adventures

While you teach your children to tackle math monsters, you also need to be teaching them to solve problems.

Math problems can seem impossible at first glance. Students need to learn basic tactics of creative reasoning to help them attack the difficult problems they meet, whether in a textbook or in daily life. Then, armed with these problem-solving skills and the arithmetic they have been studying, your children will be ready to meet any mathematical challenge.

Writing to learn math

Encourage your students to keep a ***Math Adventures Journal.*** Writing things down is a good way to learn. As children put the ideas in their own words on paper, they develop and reinforce their understanding of difficult concepts.

When students write about math problems, they experience math in a completely new way. According to math teacher and writing advocate Joan Countryman, "Writing seems to free them of the idea that math is a collection of right answers owned by the teacher—a body of knowledge that she will dispense in chunks and that they have to swallow and digest."[27]

A math journal is more like a scientist's lab book than like a diary. It's a place to store ideas, hypotheses, things you've tried or things you want to try, and especially the things you tried that didn't work. Often, analyzing a failed approach will give your student the key to finding the right solution.

These notes come in handy when solving other problems later, even problems that seem unrelated to each other. A few months ago, I was working on a problem about drawing chords (lines that cut across a circle) with various endpoints. I was stumped until I recognized a connection between this problem and one I had worked on the year before. *That* problem had been about organizing bowling pins in triangles—a totally different situation—yet it gave me the key I needed to find a solution.

If I hadn't been writing my ideas down, I probably would have given up on the problem without ever noticing the connection that solved it.

As writer and teacher William Zinsser said, "Writing is the logical arrangement of thought. Writing is how we think our way into a subject and make it our own."[28]

What should students write about?

Here are some things your kids may want to include in their Math Adventures Journal...

♦ *Challenging problems*

The traditional, textbook story problem takes no creative thought. "Johnny had three baseball cards, and Tommy had seven baseball cards. How many did they have all together?" All your students have to do is take the numbers and apply the topic of the chapter. Whether it's addition or square roots, if they follow the recipe, they'll get the required answer.

A good math problem is like a mini-mystery. To solve a challenging problem, children must draw on a deep understanding of math. They might play around with the numbers or try different things. Sometimes they will have to leave the problem alone for awhile and let their sub-conscious minds work on it.

Because it often takes more than one day to figure out the solution, students should make notes. They can write down what is given in the problem and the ideas they have tried in order to solve it. They can write down their guess as to what the answer will be, and they can describe how they test to see if the guess is right.

If you have Internet access, you can find plenty of challenging problems for students of all levels at Math Forum's *Problems of the Week* site (http://forum.swarthmore.edu/pow/). Reading the answers other students send in will help your child learn how to write about math.

Another source of problems is your area's inter-library loan program. Ask your librarian to look up books on the Mathematical Olympiad competitions. A good starter book is George Lenchner's **Math Olympiad Contest Problems.**

♦ *Original problems and puzzles*

Have your students demonstrate their understanding by making up original problems based on the textbook chapter they just finished. Or if they find a library book with fun math puzzles, encourage them to make up something similar. Almost any problem or puzzle can serve as a model for your student's creativity.

For inspiration, buy **Math by Kids! A Collection of Word Problems Written by Kids for Kids of All Ages,** edited by Susan Richman. This book offers a wide range of problems, from easy ones written by preschoolers to real toughies by high school students. Our family has had a lot of fun with it.

Richman breaks the problems down into the following categories. Reading these may stimulate your student's creative juices.

- Trading, comparing, and counting things up
- Problems about food
- Working and earning
- Shopping
- Time and traveling
- Legs problems (The Heptarians have seven legs. The Nonarians have nine legs. If there are 39 legs all together, how many aliens are there?)
- Mystery numbers (Given these hints, can you guess the number?)
- Age problems (Sue is twice as old as Jane, and in three years, Jane will be the age that Sue is now. How old will Sue be then?)
- Real-life problems
- Logic puzzles
- Geometry puzzles

Don't let your children keep all the fun to themselves. Encourage them to share their creations with friends. Most students enjoy working each other's problems and puzzles.

I am always looking for student problems to challenge the readers of my bimonthly newsletter, ***Mathematical Adventures.***

(*Mathematical Adventures*, Tabletop Academy Press, 8487 Rosedale Road, Blue Mound, IL 62513.) If I use your child's problem, he will receive five free "contributor's copies" of that issue.

♦ *Explanations*

It may be one of the world's best-kept secrets, but every teacher knows it is true: The teacher always learns more than the student. Make this fact work for you by having your students play "teacher" in their Math Adventures Journal.

Ask them to write out how they would solve a problem. They should try to explain it so well that another kid could understand and follow their instructions. That means they have to explain not only what they did, but also answer these questions:

- Why does it work?
- How did they know that was the right approach?
- Will this approach always work, or is there something special that makes this problem different?

Writing an explanation is hard work, so don't expect children to be able to do it all the time. But it is important work that builds a solid understanding of problem solving. Students don't really, thoroughly know how to do something until they can explain it to someone else.

♦ *Mathematical Research*

This would include any type of open-ended mathematical problem or puzzle.

The thing that makes a problem "research" is that there is no single, right answer. Or at least, if there is, your student has to search hard to find it. He may need to try a whole lot of special cases—like mathematical experiments, starting with the simplest examples and working up to the harder ones—before he discovers the general principle of the problem.

The I Hate Mathematics! Book and **Math for Smarty Pants** by Marilyn Burns will get your elementary and middle school students started on mathematical research. These books are full of hands-on and minds-on projects.

Middle school and older students will enjoy puzzling through a series of books by British math teacher Brian Bolt.

The Amazing Mathematical Amusement Arcade, The Mathematical Funfair, A Mathematical Pandora's Box, and others offer a tremendous variety of brain teasers and math challenges. The books attract kids with their cartoon illustrations and bite-size text, but don't be fooled. These problems pack a serious mathematical punch.

John Mason wrote **Thinking Mathematically** for junior high and high school students. He offers clear, helpful advice on how to think through tough problems and what to do when you get stuck. Mason's problem-solving strategies will help students in many areas of life, not just in mathematics.

Here is a sample problem from **Thinking Mathematically:**

⇒ **Which odd numbers have an odd number of factors?**
(Strategy: Work from specific cases to a general pattern. Start by counting the factors for several odd numbers.)

If your junior high student understands arithmetic but doesn't feel ready for algebra yet, consider taking a sabbatical from textbooks. Get **Thinking Mathematically** and a bunch of Brian Bolt books and have a year of mathematical research and problem solving. Your student will build thinking skills and cover more real math than with any pre-algebra textbook.[29]

Math class, Japanese style

When researchers compared American and Japanese classrooms, they found profound differences in the way math was taught. I mentioned this study on page 10, as a multicultural example of how we can help our children learn to think. Now, let's look at it in depth.[30]

1. The Japanese teacher begins the lesson with review.
She reminds her students of things they have learned, particularly things they may need in solving the problem for that day.

2. The teacher presents the first problem.
This is something her students do *not* know how to solve. She gives them time to work on the problem. The amount of time will depend on how hard the problem is, but for the next five to fifteen minutes, each student is on his own.

3. The teacher asks students to share their solutions.
She may comment on something a student tried, or she may

offer another method for solving the problem. This discussion time is when she does most of her teaching.

4. If there is still time...

The teacher gives her students another problem. This one may require the same sort of solution, so the students can practice what they learned. But there would probably be a twist to it, so the answer isn't obvious. Again, she gives the students time to play around with the problem, then guides the class in discussing the solution.

5. Before the lesson ends...

The teacher goes over the major point once more, to make sure the students understand. She almost never assigns homework.

In all this, the teacher keeps in mind her goal: Her students must learn to think. She does not want them merely to practice the math skills they already know. She wants them to apply what they have learned, to reason their way through new situations.

Teaching home school math

Of course, our home school math lessons will not look exactly like this. Every family is different, and every home school teacher has her own style. But the major point of the study can apply to any teacher: If we want our children to learn problem-solving skills, we need to give them problems to solve, problems that are on the edge of their ability.

Then, like the Japanese teacher, we must get out of their way and let them struggle with the problems.

I find this the most difficult part of teaching. If I stay in the room and watch Deborah or Jonathan puzzle over an assignment, I want to offer advice. I don't mean to give them the answer, just a hint or two. I can't keep my big mouth shut—so I leave the room, instead. I fix a cup of coffee or check on the younger kids.

Only when a student has time to work his own way through a hard problem can he feel the "Aha!" thrill of figuring it out.

A good problem should be more than a mere exercise. It should be challenging and not too easily solved by the student, and it should require some "dreaming" time.

—Howard Eves[31]

Keys to Creative Problem Solving

Encourage children to approach a math problem as they would a jigsaw puzzle. When they start moving pieces of the puzzle around, they look for the easy parts first—perhaps the edge pieces, or the eyes. In the same way, a student should work on the easiest-to-understand parts of his problem first.

Then, as children get into a jigsaw puzzle, they may try several pieces that don't work, so they set them aside and try others. Likewise, a problem-solving student is not discouraged by mistakes or false starts—he knows mistakes are just part of the game.

Key #1: Visualize the situation.

How hard would it be to put together a jigsaw puzzle without the picture on the box top? Impossible!

When students can make a picture in their minds of what is going on in the problem, they usually find that problem much easier to solve. I encourage my children to draw a picture, or to explain back to me what they think is happening.

Preschoolers who solve oral story problems learn early to visualize situations. School children who do their textbook work orally further develop this skill.

Key #2: Apply common sense.

If you have a red puzzle piece, it probably doesn't go in the sky unless your picture is a sunset. That's common sense, right?

Arithmetic knowledge is important in solving math problems—but not nearly so important as common sense. This is why I stress understanding instead of rules.

Encourage students to ask themselves as they work, "Does this answer make sense?"

And most of all, enjoy the challenge!

Like a jigsaw puzzle, math can be mind-stretching fun.

Remember that mathematics is mental play. If your children get a good taste of that "Aha!" feeling—the thrill of solving a challenging problem—you won't be able to keep them away from math.

Math monsters, watch out! Here come our problem-solving kids.

The only way to learn mathematics is to do mathematics.

The mathematician at work makes vague guesses, visualizes broad generalizations, and jumps to unwarranted conclusions. He arranges and rearranges his ideas, and he becomes convinced of their truth long before he can write down a logical proof.

The deductive stage, writing the result down and writing its rigorous proof, is relatively trivial once the real insight arrives. It is more like the draftsman's work, not the architect's

—*Paul Halmos*[32]

Appendixes

- A Sidestep into History
- Math Games & Computers
- Where to Find It
- Answers to Sample Problems
- Notes and References

A Sidestep into History

In 1931, Kurt Gödel published a short paper that shook the mathematical world. He proved that nobody could ever turn arithmetic into a complete and consistent logical system. It is impossible.

Gödel's Incompleteness Theorem has been called "one of the greatest intellectual accomplishments of the 20th century." (Abe Shenitzer[33])

Bertrand Russell had devoted his life to systemizing math and logic, but Gödel's proof threw his work in shambles...

> "But," you might say,
> "none of this shakes my belief that 2 and 2 are 4."
>
> You are quite right, except in marginal cases—
> and it is only in marginal cases that you are doubtful
> whether a certain animal is a dog
> or a certain length is less than a meter.
>
> Two must be two of something,
> and the proposition "2 and 2 are 4" is useless
> unless it can be applied.
>
> Two dogs and two dogs are certainly four dogs,
> but cases arise in which you are doubtful
> whether two of them are dogs.
>
> "Well, at any rate there are four animals," you may say.
> But there are microorganisms concerning which
> it is doubtful whether they are animals or plants.
>
> "Well, then living organisms," you say.
> But there are things of which it is doubtful
> whether they are living organisms or not.
>
> You will be driven into saying:
> "Two entities and two entities are four entities."
>
> When you have told me what you mean by "entity,"
> we will resume the argument.
>
> —Bertrand Russell[34]

Math Games & Computers

Math games come in two flavors: *drill* and *strategy*. A typical drill game is the card game War, for greater-than, less-than practice. A common strategy game is tic-tac-toe. (After your children master the basic game, try graph paper for a bigger playing field and go for four or five in a row.)

Getting the math facts straight

You can make up your own drill games with ***math cards***, a normal poker deck with the jokers and face cards removed. With younger children, play *Go Fish* with a twist: collect tens and pairs that make ten. If you have a six, for instance, fish for a four to match it.

With older children, play *Twenty-Four*: Deal four cards per hand, and try to use all your cards in a long equation that makes 24. You can add, subtract, multiply, or divide, but only use each card once. For example, a hand of 7, 4, 3, and 9 could make $(9 \times 3) - 7 + 4 = 24$ or $(9 - 7) \times 3 \times 4 = 24$. If nobody can make an equation, discard that hand and try again.

You will want a variety of games to keep math drill fun. Homemade games are great. [For elementary-level math games, check out the book **Games for Math** by Peggy Kaye.] Still, sometimes it is fun to play with a glossy, store-bought game. No family has time to play every game on the market, but with many costing less than $10, most home school families can afford two or three.

Avoid the games that look like dressed-up flash cards. They get boring fast. Here are some winners from the school supply catalogs:

- ★ ***1-2-3 Oy!*** (arithmetic card games)
- ★ ***24*** (like Twenty-Four, above)
- ★ ***Arithmechips*** (multiplication tables)
- ★ ***Bone Up on Math*** (like 24, but with a variable target number)
- ★ ***Continuo*** (a strategy game for all ages, no reading required, but keeping score is good addition practice)
- ★ ***Dutch Blitz*** (fast-paced card game)
- ★ ***Hive Alive*** (comparing fractions, decimals, and negatives)
- ★ ***Max-It*** (positive and negative numbers)
- ★ ***Polyhedra Dice Games*** (boxed set: 20 dice, 24 games)
- ★ ***'Smath*** (math equations, Scrabble style)
- ★ ***Tens*** (a domino-style addition game)
- ★ ***True Math*** (board game of real-world math trivia)
- ★ ***The Wonder Number Game*** (hundred chart—for counting, multiplication, and number patterns)
- ★ ***Yahtzee*** (traditional favorite)

Exercising those mental muscles

Strategy games teach thinking skills and help break through the "I can't do it" feeling of math anxiety. Because they combine a relief from tedious textbook work with the challenge of seriously creative thinking, strategy games are the best medicine available to revive a mathematically discouraged child.

There are so many strategy games available, with new ones appearing every year, that I won't even try to list them all. One excellent game for players of all ages, combining logical strategy with visual perception, is the card game *Set*. Look in the department store for old favorites like *Othello* and newer games like *Traverse*. Then send for school supply catalogs for more ideas. (Strategy games make wonderful gifts.)

Don't forget puzzles, like *Block by Block*, *Visual Brainstorms* card sets, or the *Rubik's Cube*. A good puzzle is a strategy game for one player.

Begin teaching strategy games in second or third grade, when children can handle abstract thinking. Younger children may be able to learn the rules, but they can't think through the moves. They play wildly and trust to blind chance.

Look in library books for folk games from around the world. Introduce one or two new games per month, with plenty of time to practice. It will not be long until the kids are picking the games up and playing on their own.

With any luck, you will never hear "There's nothing to do!" again.

Hiring some hi-tech help

Computer programs can teach math ideas, but my children find the drill games tiresome. The best programs are games that make the player think: *Civilization II*, the *Dr. Brain* series, *The Incredible Machine*, the shareware game *Kye*, *Lemmings* in all their misadventures, *The Logical Journey of the Zoombinis*, *The Oregon Trail*, *SimCity* and its spin-offs, *TesselMania*, *Tetris*, *Thinkin' Things*, *Triazzle*...

While we are on the topic of computers, teenagers should learn to use a word processor and spreadsheet. They may also want to work with a graphing or CAD (computer-aided drafting) program—especially if they are planning a technical career.

Anyone who likes brainteasers will probably enjoy computer programming. Programming encourages logical thinking, working through a problem systematically, and precision. Even the tiniest typo may cause your program to crash, which can be terribly discouraging. The challenge is fun, though, and not too hard if you can find a mentor who will help with de-bugging.

Where to Find It

You can find almost anything in a school supply catalog. Most of the math resources I recommend in the Homeschool Math Manuals are available through the mail from one of these first four suppliers:

* Rainbow Resource Center

Route 1 Box 159A, Toulon, IL 61483. www.rainbowresource.com or 1-888-841-3456. Books and more at discount prices. Don't miss the Logic section of their catalog. They also sell used books.

* Home School Resource Center

1425 East Chocolate Ave., Hershey, PA 17033. www.hsrc.com or (717) 533-1669. Harold Jacobs textbooks and **Math by Kids**. HSRC has a small catalog, but they carry several interesting things that are hard to find elsewhere. Their website is helpful, with product pictures and descriptions.

* Nasco

901 Janesville Avenue, PO Box 901, Fort Atkinson, WI 53538-0901. 1-800-558-9595 or www.enasco.com. Aimed at public school teachers and department heads, so they sell tons of supplies, reference books, and equipment. Ask for their math catalog.

* MindWare

2720 Patton Road, Roseville, MN 55113-1138. 1-800-999-0398 or www.mindwareonline.com. "For the other 90% of your brain..." Strategy games, lateral thinking puzzles, brain teaser books and more. A great source for gifts!

I have a few other places I like to shop. You may want to send for these catalogs, too:

Critical Thinking Books and Software

PO Box 448, Pacific Grove, CA, 93950-0448. 1-800-458-4849 or www.criticalthinking.com. A wonderful collection of workbooks to build thinking skills across the curriculum—I wish I could afford to buy them all! The website offers free demo versions of their software.

Dover Publications

31 East 2nd Street, Mineola, NY 11501-3582. Affordable books of all sorts. Try their "Puzzles, Games, and Chess Books", "Pictorial Archive", and "Children's Books" catalogs.

The Elijah Company

1053 Eldridge Loop, Crossville, TN 38558. www.elijahco.com or 1-888-235-4524. They carry the Harold Jacobs books, but their catalog is best known for its overview of several homeschool teaching styles.

Family Things

19363 Willamette Drive # 237, West Linn, OR 97068. (503) 727-5473 or www.singaporemath.com. Singapore math and science textbooks. The contents of the books are listed on the website, to help you choose the right level.

Follett Educational Services

1433 International Parkway, Woodridge, IL 60517. www.fes.follett.com or 1-800-621-4272. Searchable website of used textbooks, including Howard Jacobs textbooks.

Games magazine

PO Box 2031, Marion, OH 43305-2031. 1-800-426-3768. Games, puzzles, strategy, word play, awful puns, and killer crosswords, from upper-elementary to graduate-level stumpers. For families with older students, this is an excellent non-textbook resource for math, logic, and language skills. $33/year (9 issues).

John Holt's Bookstore

2380 Massachusetts Ave., Suite 104, Cambridge, MA 02140-1884. 1-888-925-9298. A very small catalog of books that encourage independent learning. Includes Harold Jacob texts.

The Teaching Company

7405 Alban Station Court, Suite A-107, Springfield, VA 22150-2318. www.teachco.com or 1-800-832-2412. Math courses on videotape with "SuperStar Teachers." Expensive, but they do offer a money-back satisfaction guarantee. If you are nervous about teaching high school math, you may want to consider them. With an enthusiastic teacher talking about a subject he loves, students can learn almost anything.

Math Products Plus

PO Box 64, San Carlos, CA 94070. (650) 593-2839. Theoni Pappas books, including both **Mathematics Calendars** (adult and children's), which provide lots of problem-solving practice.

Answers to Sample Problems

Factoring challenge, page 25

- A number less than 48 that makes five rectangles = 36.
- Numbers less than 100 that makes more than five rectangles = 60, 72, 84, and 96.

Hands-on division, page 37

396 ÷ 18 = ?

Area ÷ up = over.

Start by counting out the area: 3 flats, 9 rods, 6 ones.

Build a rectangle that is 18 up. Set down a flat and lay 8 rods horizontally above it—that is 18 x 10. Put a second flat next to the first, which makes 20 over. But you only have one rod to go with this one. You need seven more rods to make 18 up. Change the last flat for 10 rods, and finish your second column. Now your rectangle is 18 x 20.

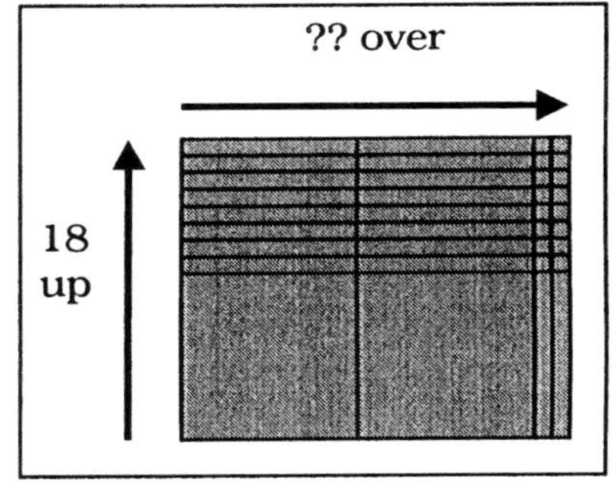

Lay the last three rods vertically beside the second flat, and arrange the ones above them. Can you finish the rectangle? No, the ones will not fill in the corner. Trade one of your rods for 10 ones. Now the ones should fit. Your answer is: 396 ÷ 18 = 22.

Mastering the rules, page 41

1-4. Multiplication and division are related operations, since division is multiplication done backwards. Most of the rules that apply to multiplication also work for division. But addition and subtraction are different from multiplication, so we shouldn't be surprised that the rules are different, too. Adding and subtracting fractions is like counting more or fewer pieces of pizza. Multiplying and dividing fractions is like slicing the pizza into different-sized pieces.

5. Of course it matters which fraction you flip. Division is always that way: 6 ÷ 3 is not the same as 3 ÷ 6.

Equivalent fractions, page 49

- What if they cut 1/2 pizza into four pieces—what size would the pieces be? 1/2 = 4/8. If there are four pieces in 1/2, there would be eight in the whole pizza, so the pieces are eighths.

- What if they cut five pieces? 1/2 = 5/10.
- What if they cut 1/3 pizza into 100 pieces—what would they have then? 1/3 = 100/300.
- One fourth of a pizza will make how many 64ths? 1/4 = 16/64.
- One third is how many 390ths? 1/3 = 130/390.

The epitaph of Diophantus, page 52

This riddle is definitely *not* easy. To solve this, we need a little algebra. Pretend that D stands for the number of years that Diophantus lived.

He was a boy for 1/6 of his life, or $D/6$ years. Then he was a youth for 1/12 of his life, until he got a beard—that's $D/12$ years. After another seventh, he got married—$D/7$ more years. And he had been married 5 years when his son was born.

This is where it really gets tricky. The phrase "when he had reached the measure of half his father's life" means that the son lived half as long as the father lived *total*. That adds $D/2$ more years to Diophantus's life.

[When I first read this problem, I thought this phrase meant the son was half as old as the father was *when the son died*. But if you calculate it that way, the answer doesn't come out even. Since Diophantus is famous among mathematicians for studying equations that always come out even—without fractions—I had to change my interpretation.]

Finally, Diophantus lived four more years after his son died.

Put this all together to make an algebraic equation for how long Diophantus lived:

$$D = \frac{D}{6} + \frac{D}{12} + \frac{D}{7} + 5 + \frac{D}{2} + 4$$

What a mess of fractions! Those old Greeks may not have known place value, but they were crafty geniuses. Can you imagine working this out in Roman numerals?

We need to find a common denominator. Since 12 x 7 = 84, convert all the fractions into the 84ths family. Remember that whole numbers like 5 and 4 and D are fractions, too: 5 = 5/1, 4 = 4/1, and $D = D/1$.

$$\frac{84D}{84} = \frac{14D}{84} + \frac{7D}{84} + \frac{12D}{84} + \frac{420}{84} + \frac{42D}{84} + \frac{336}{84}$$

Now that everything is in the same fraction family, we can count up the numerators.

$$\frac{84D}{84} = \frac{14D + 7D + 12D + 420 + 42D + 336}{84}$$

...which means that...

$$84D = 14D + 7D + 12D + 420 + 42D + 336$$

...and...

$$84D = 75D + 756$$

$$84D - 75D = 75D + 756 - 75D$$

$$9D = 756 \text{ and finally : } D = 84$$

So Diophantus lived to be 84 years old, and his son died at age 42.

Monster division fractions, page 66

270/45 = 6   1344/168 = 8   1584/792 = 2

A fraction is a comparison, page 69

- $1/2 = x/16$, so $x = 8$.
- $13/52 = n/12$, so $n = 3$.

Dividing by a fraction, page 75

Prove that $x \div (a/b) = x(b/a)$. Here is one way to do it:

$$x \div \frac{a}{b} = x \Big/ \frac{a}{b}$$ The line in a fraction means "divided by."

$$= x \cdot 1 \Big/ \frac{a}{b}$$ Anything times one is unchanged.

$$= x\left(1 \Big/ \frac{a}{b}\right)$$ You can multiply numbers in any order.

$$= x\left(\frac{b}{a}\right)$$ Definition of reciprocal fractions.

Original problems, page 79

- How old will Sue be then? She will be nine years old.
- How many aliens are there?
  There have to be five aliens: three Heptarians and two Nonarians.

Mathematical Research, page 81

Which odd numbers have an odd number of factors?

(If you need to review factors, see page 25.) Factors usually come in pairs, so *most* numbers have an even number of factors. The exceptions are the square numbers, because the square root is a single factor.

Notes and References

I love quotations, don't you? Everything I could ever want to say has probably been said sometime by someone else (who didn't think of it first, either). At least a few of those people had a wonderful way with words. Some of the quotations in this book are from my own reading. Others are gleaned from two Internet sites that I visit often to browse...

Furman University's *Mathematical Quotation Server* (MQS):
www.math.furman.edu/~mwoodard/mqs/mquot.shtml

Mathematical and Educational Quotation Server (MEQS) at Westfield State College:
bondo.wsc.mass.edu/dept/math/faculty/fleron/quotes/quohome.htm

---

[1] Jonathan Kozol, at Westfield State College's 157th Commencement. MEQS.

[2] Charles Dickens, 11/5/1857 speech. MEQS.

[3] Mary Beth Ruskai, from "From the Editor," ***Notices of the American Mathematical Society***, vol. 42, no. 7, July 1995. MEQS.

[4] Earl Wilson. Quoted in Donald Spencer's **Dictionary of Mathematical Quotations**, Camelot Publishing Co., 1998.

[5] Edward Rothstein, "Making Math Magical," ***Family Life***, Sept./Oct. 1996.

[6] James W. Stigler and James Hiebert, "Understanding and improving classroom mathematics instruction: An overview of the TIMSS video study," ***Phi Delta Kappan***, Sept. 1997, v78 n1.

[7] Anonymous. Quoted in Donald Spencer's **Dictionary of Mathematical Quotations**, Camelot Publishing Co., 1998.

[8] You can make base ten blocks at home, but they will be trickier to use than plastic or wooden sets because the pieces slide under each other. Glue one-centimeter grid paper to sheets of construction paper, then laminate. Cut out unit squares for the ones, rods of ten squares each, and big 10 x 10 squares (called *flats*) for hundreds.

For instructions on using base ten blocks to help students understand algebra, see my book **Algebra for Anyone**.

[9] Actually, the Babylonians did use a form of place value. This enabled them to perform accurate astronomical calculations, calculate powers and roots, and even solve quadratic equations. I am not sure why this system

was lost. Perhaps the Greek mathematicians were too proud to learn from barbarians.

[10] Renan, Ernest. **Souvenirs d'enfance et de jeunesse.** MQS

[11] Tom Lehrer. Quoted in Donald Spencer's **Dictionary of Mathematical Quotations,** Camelot Publishing Co., 1998.

[12] Anonymous. In **Mathematical Ideas** by Charles D. Miller, Vern E. Heeren, and E. John Hernsby, Jr. HarperCollins College Publishers, New York, 1994.

[13] John Napier, **A Description of the Marvelous Law of Logarithms.** Napier's invention of logarithms made calculating easier for generations of mathematicians, scientists, and engineers. Quoted in the *MacTutor History of Mathematics Archive*:
www-history.mcs.st-and.ac.uk/history/Mathematicians/Napier.html

[14] Numbers that can make squares (such as 4 = 2 x 2 or 16 = 4 x 4) are called *square* numbers.

Numbers that can only make lines (such as 13 = 1 x 13) are called *prime* numbers.

[15] Andrew Wiles, from the BBC program "Fermat's Last Theorem" (broadcast in the U.S. on PBS's ***NOVA*** as "The Proof"), by Simon Singh and John Lynch. MEQS.

[16] Plato. MQS.

[17] Charles Darwin. Quoted in the *Platonic Realms Quote Collection*:
www.mathacademy.com/platonic_realms/quotes/Quotfram.html

[18] Tolstoy, Count Lev Nikolgevich (1828-1920). In H. Eves **Return to Mathematical Circles,** Boston: Prindle, Weber and Schmidt, 1989. MQS.

[19] Diophantus [His epitaph]. In Ivor Thomas "Greek Mathematics," in J. R. Newman (ed.) **The World of Mathematics,** New York: Simon and Schuster, 1956. MQS.

[20] ***Time*** magazine, June 18, 1956. Quoted by George Polyá in **How To Solve It,** Princeton University Press, 1973.

[21] Lynn Arthur Steen, from **On the Shoulders of Giants.** MEQS.

[22] Mary Baratta-Lorton. Quoted in **About Teaching Mathematics: A K-8 Resource,** by Marilyn Burns. MEQS.

[23] George Polyá, **How To Solve It,** Princeton University Press, 1973.

[24] As with the SAT grammar ratios, math ratios may be written with a colon instead of a fraction line. 1:2 = 3:6.

[25] A reciprocal may also be called an *inverse.* The inverse of 2 is ½.

[26] John Dewey. MEQS.

[27] Joan Countryman. Quoted by William Zinsser in **Writing to Learn.**

[28] William Zinsser, **Writing to Learn: How to Write—and Think—Clearly About Any Subject at All.** Harper & Row Publishers, New York, 1988.

[29] Pre-algebra textbooks introduce the concepts of negative numbers, coordinate graphing, and variables (letters that stand for unknown numbers.) Most children who understand arithmetic and are used to thinking their way through problems do not need a pre-algebra textbook.

[30] James W. Stigler and James Hiebert, "Understanding and improving classroom mathematics instruction: An overview of the TIMSS video study," ***Phi Delta Kappan*** Sept. 1997, v78 n1.

[31] Howard Eves, **An Introduction to the History of Mathematics.** Saunders College Publishing, 1990.

[32] Paul Halmos. Quoted in **Out of the Mouths of Mathematicians,** by Rosemary Schmalz. MEQS.

[33] Abe Shenitzer, from "Teaching Mathematics," in **Mathematics Tomorrow,** ed. L. A. Steen. MEQS.

[34] Bertrand Russell. Quoted in N. Rose, **Mathematical Maxims and Minims,** Rome Press, Raleigh, NC, 1988. MQS.

Tabletop Academy Press presents:

Homeschool Math Manuals

1—Aha! How to Teach Math So Kids Get It

Lay a foundation for success in math by building your child's problem-solving skills. Discover how toys, games, and library books can help children enjoy the challenge of creative mathematical thinking—and when to make the transition to textbooks.

2—Mastering the Math Monsters: Factors, Fractions, and Long Division

Math monsters are those scary topics of textbook arithmetic, the things that go *thump!* in the mind. But the math monsters need not frighten your child, if you teach with these hands-on games and manipulatives.

3—Algebra for Anyone: Getting a Handle on Abstract Math

Children can begin to learn algebra as early as third grade using manipulatives, but without them even high school students may struggle. With step-by-step instructions and examples, this book takes you from solving simple equations to factoring quadratic polynomials.

4—Gotcha! Strategy Games for Math and Logic

Games encourage a creatively logical approach to solving problems. When children play strategy games, they learn to enjoy the challenge of thinking hard. Here are more than 20 games your family can enjoy at home or in the car.

Bible Study Basics

Glory and Grace: Getting Kids into the Bible

Are you looking for a Bible study program where you and your children actually study the Bible, rather than a book about the Bible? Passages focus on the character of God, so children come to know and love Him—His holiness and grace, our sin and need, His great redemption.

The Promised Savior: A Jesse Tree Christmas Devotional

Even before the creation of the universe, God knew that Christmas was coming. The Jesse Tree is a 25-day Old Testament survey course for Advent. Along with each reading, the book gives instructions for a Christmas tree ornament your children can make.